Journeys Through the Siddur

יוֹם שַׁבָּת Shabbat Morning

Table of Contents

ISBN #1-891662-41-4

Copyright © 2004 Torah Aura Productions

Copyright © Lane Yerkes and Christine Tripp

Photograph Credits: Page 3—©Image Source/Elektra Vision/PictureQuest; page 7—©Orion Press/Stone; page 14—©Tim Page/CORBIS; page 22—©Dynamic Graphics Inc.; page 27—©Tyler Stableford/The Image Bank; page 35—©Chuck Fishman/The Image Bank; page 41—©Bettmann/CORBIS; page 46—©Frans Lemmens/The Image Bank; page 56—©Sarah Leen/National Geographics; page 63—©Steve Campbell/PhotoDisc Green; page 73—©Dave Bartruff/CORBIS; page 78—©Pictorial Library of Bible Lands; page 82—©AFP/CORBIS.

Torah Aura Productions ◆ 4423 Fruitland Avenue, Los Angeles, CA 90058
(800) BE-Torah ◆ (800) 238-6724 ◆ (323) 585-7312 ◆ fax (323) 585-0327
E-MAIL <misrad@torahaura.com> ◆ Visit the Torah Aura website at www.torahaura.com

MANUFACTURED IN CHINA

בָּרְכוּ

The בָּרְכוּ is the way the people in a synagogue become a congregation. It is the way that individuals become a prayer community. There are times for Jews to pray alone, but in our services we pray together.

The בָּרְכוּ is an invitation. It is a call and response. That means that the prayer leader asks a question and the congregation answers together. In answering they become a community.

The leader invites: בָּרְכוּ אֶת־יי הַמְבֹרָךְ. Are you ready to say "בְּרָכוֹת" to יי?

When everyone says: רָךְ לְעוֹלָם וָעֶד בָּרוּךְ יי הַמְב, the congregation is created and the community is formed.

The answer means: Yes, God deserves בְּרָכוֹת forever and always.

This pattern of call and response as an invitation is used two other times in Jewish life. The exact same words are used to begin the blessings before the reading of the Torah. And very similar words (and the same pattern) are used to begin *Birkat ha-Mazon*, the blessing after eating that is said only when a community (at least three people) eats together.

Why do you think these three events—praying, reading Torah, and the end of a meal—require a special way of forming community?

The בָּרְכוּ is said only if there is a minyan, a group of at least ten people praying together.

Can you see the three-letter root בּרך in these words?
It is found in every בְּרָכָה.

בָּרוּךְ   בָּרְכוּ   הַמְבֹרָךְ

blessed = בָּרוּךְ

bless (plural) = בָּרְכוּ

the One Who is blessed = הַמְבֹרָךְ

CLUE: ך = כ = בּ

Practice these words and circle all the words that contain the root בּרך.

1. מַלְכֵי   מֶלֶךְ   בָּרְכוּ   כְּבוֹד   מַלְכוּתוֹ   בָּרוּךְ

2. בָּרֵךְ   מַלְכֵּנוּ   הַמְבֹרָךְ   שְׁמַע   וָעֶד   הַמְּלָכִים

3. לִבְרָכָה   בָּרָא   בְּרוּכִים   אֵין   מְבֹרָךְ   כְּבוֹד

4. בָּרְכוּנִי   הָעוֹלָם   מֶלֶךְ   בִּרְכַּת   אַתָּה   בָּרוּךְ

5. בְּמִצְוֹתָיו   בָּרְכֵנוּ   בְּרָכוֹת   אֵין   כְּמַלְכֵּנוּ

Write in the missing root letters.

6. בָּרוּ___   7. הַמְ___רָךְ   8. בָּרְ___ו

9. בְּ___כַּת   10. בְּרָ___וֹת   11. ___רוּכִים

Review the vocabulary and make your best guess at the meaning of the בָּרְכוּ.

Take your best guess at these meanings. Your teacher will help you fill in the parts you don't yet know.

בָּרְכוּ אֶת־יי הַמְבֹרָךְ

 אֶת־יי .

words

Adonai = יי

and more = וָעֶד

before = אֶת
direct object

word parts

the = הַ   to = לְ

בָּרוּךְ יי הַמְבֹרָךְ לְעוֹלָם וָעֶד.

וָעֶד. לְ יי

How to Dance the בָּרְכוּ

We say the בָּרְכוּ with our bodies as well as with our mouths.

Take a breath and let it out slowly. It should make you feel alive. A good breath goes through your whole body. In Hebrew, one word for breath is connected to the word for soul. In Genesis we learned that we come alive when God breathes our soul into our body. The first secret to saying the בָּרְכוּ is breathing and feeling the breath run through your body, reminding you of the gift of life.

The second secret to saying the בָּרְכוּ is knowing that the Hebrew root בּרך is also the word for knees. We bow when we say the בָּרְכוּ. We bow deeply, just like a person who is entering a

room where a king or queen is waiting. We bow by first bending our knees and then bending our spine.

The last secret to saying the בָּרְכוּ is remembering that it is a call and response. We stand while the leader bows and says the first line, "בָּרְכוּ." We bend and bow when we say our line, "בָּרוּךְ יי." We breathe out as we bend our knees and bow. We breathe back in as we come back up—unbending and unbowing.

The First בָּרְכוּ

All Jews used to gather on a mountain in Jerusalem to worship and come close to God. Three times a year everyone would go to the Temple. At those times, Jews felt like they really belonged, and at those moments God felt very close. Then it was over. The Babylonians conquered Jerusalem, and the Temple was destroyed and left in ruins. The Jews were carried away as slaves, and the mountain where the Jews had gathered was empty. Israel was in exile.

It took seventy years to get permission to return. At first, only a few Jews left their new homes and their new businesses to become pioneers. They began to rebuild the Land of Israel and rebuild the Temple, but it did not go well. There were many problems. Finally, two new leaders came from Babylonia. They were Ezra and Nehemiah. To bring people together they held an eight-day festival in the center of the unfinished Temple courtyard. For three of those days, for the first time ever, the Torah was read from beginning to end.

At the beginning of this gathering, when everyone was standing in the unfinished court-yard waiting to see what would happen, the Levites got up on the stage. The Levites were the singers and musicians who led services in the Temple. They broke the silence with words that were more or less the בָּרְכוּ. The people answered with their part. When this בָּרְכוּ ended, the exile was over. Israel was again one people, and they again had a home.

(Reuven Hammer's book, *Entering Jewish Prayer, A Guide to Personal Devotion and the Worship Service*)

Questions

1. How did saying the בָּרְכוּ end the exile?
2. How can remembering this first בָּרְכוּ in the unfinished Temple help us to know where to point our hearts when we say the בָּרְכוּ?

יוֹצֵר אוֹר

יוֹצֵר אוֹר is:

- the first of two בְּרָכוֹת before the שְׁמַע in the morning,
- a בְּרָכָה about the creation of light,
- a memory of the Garden of Eden,
- a look at good and evil in the world,
- a glance at a better future.

The traditional יוֹצֵר אוֹר is a long prayer that gets even longer on Shabbat. In the Reform Siddur (and in some other prayerbooks), a shorter version is used. We will look at only part of the prayer in this book.

The יוֹצֵר אוֹר is about light. Light means many things. Light was the first thing that God created. Everything started with light. When we thank God for making the light, we are also thanking God for all of creation.

When we speak of light and darkness, we are also talking about good and evil. Darkness stands for evil, the place where God seems to be missing. Light is the place where people are connected to God and do what is right.

Light also stands for learning and wisdom. When people gain knowledge, we call them "enlightened." For Jews, the Torah is the central wisdom that God wants us to have. We also say and sing תּוֹרָה אוֹרָה, the "Torah is light".

A midrash that you will read later in this chapter tells us that Adam and Eve were the first ones to say the יוֹצֵר אוֹר. The first יוֹצֵר אוֹר was in the Garden of Eden. It spoke of creation and good and evil.

The יוֹצֵר אוֹר is a very long prayer. Here are a few parts of the text to practice.

BLESSED are You, ADONAI	בָּרוּךְ אַתָּה יי	1.
our God, RULER of the COSMOS	אֱלֹהֵינוּ מֶלֶךְ הָעוֹלָם	2.
The One-Who-Radiates LIGHT and creates DARKNESS	יוֹצֵר אוֹר וּבוֹרֵא חֹשֶׁךְ	3.
The One-Who-Makes PEACE and Who Creates EVERYTHING.	עֹשֶׂה שָׁלוֹם וּבוֹרֵא אֶת הַכֹּל.	4.
The One-Who-LIGHTS the earth	הַמֵּאִיר לָאָרֶץ	5.
and her residents in mercy,	וְלַדָּרִים עָלֶיהָ בְּרַחֲמִים	6.
in GOODNESS (God) makes ANEW	וּבְטוּבוֹ מְחַדֵּשׁ	7.
every single day—always—the makings of CREATION.	בְּכָל יוֹם תָּמִיד מַעֲשֵׂה בְרֵאשִׁית.	8.
Your makings are great, ADONAI,	מַה רַבּוּ מַעֲשֶׂיךָ יי	9.
You made all of them WISELY	כֻּלָּם בְּחָכְמָה עָשִׂיתָ	10.
the earth is filled with Your possessions.	מָלְאָה הָאָרֶץ קִנְיָנֶךָ.	11.
Be BLESSED, ADONAI, our God	תִּתְבָּרַךְ יי אֱלֹהֵינוּ	12.
for the glory of the makings of Your hands	עַל שֶׁבַח מַעֲשֵׂה יָדֶיךָ	13.
and for the brightness of the LIGHTS which You made	וְעַל מְאוֹרֵי אוֹר שֶׁעָשִׂיתָ	14.
May they exalt You—So be it!	יְפָאֲרוּךָ סֶלָה.	15.
BLESSED are You, ADONAI,	בָּרוּךְ אַתָּה יי	16.
The ONE-Who-Radiates LIGHTS.	יוֹצֵר הַמְּאוֹרוֹת.	17.

Can you see the three letters ברא in these words?

בְּרִיאָה   לִבְרֹא   בּוֹרֵא

create = בּוֹרֵא

to create = לִבְרֹא

a creation = בְּרִיאָה

Practice these words and circle all the words that contain the root ברא.

1. בּוֹרֵא   בָּרוּךְ   כָּבוֹד   בּוֹרְאֶךָ   מַלְכוּתוֹ   הַמְבֹרָךְ

2. פְּרִי   הַגֶּפֶן   בָּרָא   יוֹצֵר   אוֹר   וּבוֹרֵא   חֹשֶׁךְ

Can you see the three letters אוֹר in these words? Sometimes the וֹ drops out.

מְאוֹרוֹת   מְאוֹרֵי   הַמֵּאִיר

the One-Who lights = הַמֵּאִיר

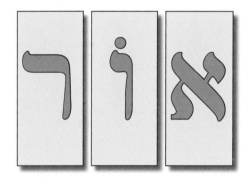

the lights of = מְאוֹרֵי

lights = מְאוֹרוֹת

Circle the words with the root אוֹר.

3. אוֹר   יוֹצֵר   בּוֹרֵא   מְאוֹרוֹת   הֵאִיר   הַבְּרִיאוֹת

4. הוּאַר   תָּמִיד   עוֹלָם   תָּאִיר   לְאוֹרוֹ   תּוֹרָה   אוֹרָה

9

Practice these words and phrases.

1. הָאֵר לִבְרֹא הָאָרֶץ לְהַדְלִיק אֱלֹהִים

2. מִצְוָה בָּרְכוּ בְּרִיאָה בְּרֵאשִׁית כְּמַלְכֵּנוּ

3. שָׁלוֹם לָאָרֶץ יָאוֹר הָאֵשׁ מְאוֹרֵי עַל

4. הַבְּרִיאוֹת לִבְרֹא הָאָרֶץ לְהַדְלִיק אֱלֹהִים

5. טוֹבִים מְאוֹרוֹת שֶׁבָּרָא אֱלֹהֵינוּ

6. הַמֵּאִיר לָאָרֶץ וְלַדָּרִים עָלֶיהָ בְּרַחֲמִים

7. וְהָאֵר עֵינֵינוּ בְּתוֹרָתֶךָ וְדַבֵּק לִבֵּנוּ בְּמִצְוֹתֶיךָ

8. יוֹצֵר אוֹר וּבוֹרֵא חֹשֶׁךְ עֹשֶׂה שָׁלוֹם וּבוֹרֵא אֶת הַכֹּל

9. בּוֹרֵא יוֹם וָלַיְלָה גּוֹלֵל אוֹר מִפְּנֵי חֹשֶׁךְ וְחֹשֶׁךְ מִפְּנֵי אוֹר

10. בָּרוּךְ אַתָּה יי אֱלֹהֵינוּ מֶלֶךְ הָעוֹלָם בּוֹרֵא מְאוֹרֵי הָאֵשׁ

Review the vocabulary and make your best guess at the meaning of this part of יוֹצֵר אוֹר.

חֹשֶׁךְ   אוֹר   עוֹלָם   מֶלֶךְ   אַתָּה   ברך

בָּרוּךְ אַתָּה יי אֱלֹהֵינוּ מֶלֶךְ הָעוֹלָם

יוֹצֵר אוֹר וּבוֹרֵא חֹשֶׁךְ

עֹשֶׂה שָׁלוֹם וּבוֹרֵא אֶת-הַכֹּל.

_____

_____

_____

word parts	words	verbs
the = הַ/הָ	Adonai = יי	creates = בּוֹרֵא
and = וְ/וּ	our God = אֱלֹהֵינוּ	בּוֹרֵא is only for God
	do or make = עֹשֶׂה	creates = יוֹצֵר
Take your best guess at these meanings. Your teacher will help you fill in the parts you don't yet know.	peace = שָׁלוֹם	יוֹצֵר can be done by either people or God
	all = כָּל/כֹּל	

11

Adam and Eve's First Shabbat

Adam and Eve were created about two hours before sundown before the first Shabbat. In one hour, they managed to fall in love, eat the fruit from the one tree they had been told to avoid, and make God really angry.

Just before Shabbat was ready to begin, God was prepared to kick them out of the Garden. Adam and Eve were really scared. When they were created, the sun was yellow and high in the sky. Now it was blood red and sinking toward the horizon. They were terrified because they believed God was punishing them. They thought God was uncreating the world, and they would be in darkness forever.

Just as God got ready to kick them out of the Garden, Shabbat stepped in. She said, "You promised me that I would not be alone. Everyone else has a partner. Sunday has Monday. Tuesday has Wednesday. Thursday has Friday. Only I am alone. You promised me that Israel would be with me. If you kick Adam and Eve out of the Garden before they experience this Shabbat, Israel will never know how wonderful I can be. I will be too much effort, because they will not know my reward."

God agreed. "Adam and Eve can spend this Shabbat in the Garden, but then they will have to leave."

As the sun set, God showed Adam and Eve how to light Shabbat candles. This was the first fire. They then walked together around the garden and God showed off all the things that had been created. God even introduced them to Shoshana, the macaw. Together they sat down and ate Shabbat dinner. God told Adam and Eve that everything would be fine. God tucked them in to go to sleep. The midrash even tells us that "God braided Eve's hair."

The two of them heard God's words, "Things will be okay," but they did not believe them. They did not sleep at all. They tossed and turned all night. It was the longest night—I'll bet you know that kind of night. They thought and thought about what they had done and they felt really bad about the way they had acted.

The night seemed to last forever. Then suddenly there was gray at the edges of the black. Then the night was edged in blue. They could see things again. At last the edge of the sun sparked between two mountains, and Adam and Eve realized that the world had not been destroyed. As they faced the new day, their new chance, they said together, "Praised are You...the One-Who Radiates light and Creates darkness, the One-Who Makes peace and even Creates evil."

Later, God would teach Isaiah those same words. Even later, the rabbis who arranged the siddur would use them as the prayer to greet the morning light, because they knew that in some way, every morning is like that first Shabbat morning that greeted Adam and Eve. It is a chance to start over. (From the Midrash, with a touch of Danny Siegel)

Questions

1. What do you think that first Shabbat morning meant to Adam and Eve?
2. When have you felt that way?
3. How can remembering this story help you find a way to point your heart when you say this prayer?

אַהֲבָה רַבָּה

The אַהֲבָה רַבָּה is:

- the second of two morning בְּרָכוֹת before the שְׁמַע,
- a בְּרָכָה about God's love for Israel,
- a memory of Mount Sinai,
- a statement about the power of studying Torah
- a look at the relationship that Torah creates between God and Israel.

It was at Mount Sinai that God gave us the gift of Torah. Torah shows us that God loves us—because in it God gave us the wisdom we need to live a good life.

Torah makes us God's partner. When the Jews received the Torah, they agreed to work with God to make the world into the best possible place. Torah is a book of directions on how to change ourselves into the best people we can be and on how to change the world into the best place we all can make it. Torah creates a contract. When we accepted the Torah we agreed to work with God to create a world of peace, justice, freedom, and prosperity.

Mount Sinai was the moment that Israel first knew that God loved them. That love came in a book, the Torah.

The אַהֲבָה רַבָּה talks about our relationship with God. It reminds us that through the Torah we can be close to God.

14

אַהֲבָה רַבָּה

With much LOVE You have LOVED us,	1. אַהֲבָה רַבָּה אֲהַבְתָּנוּ,
Adonai, our God,	2. יי אֱלֹהֵינוּ,
With great COMPASSION and more	3. חֶמְלָה גְדוֹלָה וִיתֵרָה
You have had COMPASSION on us.	4. חָמַלְתָּ עָלֵינוּ.
Our PARENT, our Ruler,	5. אָבִינוּ מַלְכֵּנוּ,
for the sake of our PARENTS who trusted in You—	6. בַּעֲבוּר אֲבוֹתֵינוּ שֶׁבָּטְחוּ בְךָ
and whom You taught the rules of life—	7. וַתְּלַמְּדֵם חֻקֵּי חַיִּים
also (A) be gracious to us and TEACH us.	8. כֵּן תְּחָנֵּנוּ וּתְלַמְּדֵנוּ.
Our PARENT, the MERCIFUL PARENT	9. אָבִינוּ, הָאָב הָרַחֲמָן
The ONE-Who-is-MERCIFUL, (B) have MERCY on us.	10. הַמְרַחֵם, רַחֵם עָלֵינוּ
(Please) (C) give (in) our hearts	11. וְתֵן בְּלִבֵּנוּ
(1) to understand, (2) to reason, (3) to hear,	12. לְהָבִין וּלְהַשְׂכִּיל, לִשְׁמֹעַ
(4) to be TAUGHT, (5) to TEACH, (6) to keep,	13. לִלְמֹד וּלְלַמֵּד לִשְׁמֹר
(7) to do, (8) to make permanent	14. וְלַעֲשׂוֹת, וּלְקַיֵּם
all the words of the TEACHING of Your Torah	15. אֶת כָּל דִּבְרֵי תַלְמוּד תּוֹרָתֶךָ
in LOVE.	16. בְּאַהֲבָה

(D) Enlighten our eyes with Your Torah	וְהָאֵר עֵינֵינוּ בְּתוֹרָתֶךָ	17.
and (E) make Your mitzvot stick to our hearts	וְדַבֵּק לִבֵּנוּ בְּמִצְוֹתֶיךָ	18.
and (F) unify our hearts to LOVE	וְיַחֵד לְבָבֵנוּ לְאַהֲבָה	19.
and to be in AWE of Your NAME.	וּלְיִרְאָה אֶת שְׁמֶךָ.	20.
And (please) (G) don't let us be embarrassed, ever—	וְלֹא נֵבוֹשׁ לְעוֹלָם וָעֶד	21.
because in Your holy NAME	כִּי בְשֵׁם קָדְשְׁךָ	22.
which is GREAT and AWESOME we trust.	הַגָּדוֹל וְהַנּוֹרָא בָּטָחְנוּ	23.
We will REJOICE AND BE HAPPY IN YOUR SALVATION.	נָגִילָה וְנִשְׂמְחָה בִּישׁוּעָתֶךָ.	24.
(H) And (please) bring us in peace	וַהֲבִיאֵנוּ לְשָׁלוֹם	25.
from the four corners of the earth	מֵאַרְבַּע כַּנְפוֹת הָאָרֶץ,	26.
and make us go and establish our land—	וְתוֹלִיכֵנוּ קוֹמְמִיּוּת לְאַרְצֵנוּ.	27.
because You are God, The ONE-Who-Works at SALVATION	כִּי אֵל פּוֹעֵל יְשׁוּעוֹת אָתָּה,	28.
and You have CHOSEN us from all peoples	וּבָנוּ בָחַרְתָּ מִכָּל עַם	29.
and language groupings	וְלָשׁוֹן	30.
and You have brought us close to Your GREAT NAME	וְקֵרַבְתָּנוּ לְשִׁמְךָ הַגָּדוֹל	31.
in truth, so be it—	סֶלָה בֶּאֱמֶת,	32.
to give thanks to You and to Your ONENESS in LOVE.	לְהוֹדוֹת לְךָ וּלְיַחֶדְךָ בְּאַהֲבָה.	33.
BLESSED are You, Adonai,	בָּרוּךְ אַתָּה יי	34.
The ONE-Who-CHOOSES the People Israel, in LOVE.	הַבּוֹחֵר בְּעַמּוֹ יִשְׂרָאֵל בְּאַהֲבָה.	35.

Can you see the three letters **אהב** in these words?

וְאָהַבְתָּ   אֲהַבְתָּנוּ   אַהֲבָה

love = אַהֲבָה

You have loved us = אֲהַבְתָּנוּ

and you shall love = וְאָהַבְתָּ

Practice these words and phrases and circle all the words that contain the root **אהב**.

1. וְאָהַבְתָּ   קְדֻשָּׁה   יוֹצֵר   בָּרָא   קָדוֹשׁ   אוֹהֵב

2. אַהֲבַת   מַלְכוּתְךָ   אַהֲבָה   אֱלֹהֵינוּ   בִּרְכַּת

3. אָהוּב   אָהוֹב   אֲהַבְתָּנוּ   מֶלֶךְ   אֲהָבִים

4. וְיַחֵד לְבָבֵנוּ לְאַהֲבָה וּלְיִרְאָה אֶת שְׁמֶךָ

5. אַהֲבַת עוֹלָם בֵּית יִשְׂרָאֵל עַמְּךָ אָהַבְתָּ

6. אַהֲבָה רַבָּה אֲהַבְתָּנוּ יי אֱלֹהֵינוּ חֶמְלָה גְדוֹלָה וִיתֵרָה

7. וְאָהַבְתָּ אֵת יי אֱלֹהֶיךָ בְּכָל־לְבָבְךָ וּבְכָל־נַפְשְׁךָ וּבְכָל־מְאֹדֶךָ

Go back to pages 15-16 and practice the אַהֲבָה רַבָּה before you work on this page.

Word Endings

Look at the two letters נוּ
at the end of these
two words:

לְבֵּנוּ   עֵינֵינוּ
our hearts   our eyes

נוּ means "our" or "us."

Look at the letter ךָ
at the end of these
two words:

בְּתוֹרָתֶךָ   שְׁמֶךָ
Your name   Your Torah

ךָ means "your."

Circle the words that end with נוּ and underline those with ךָ.

1. עֵינֵינוּ   בְּתוֹרָתֶךָ   לְבֵּנוּ   אֲבוֹתֵינוּ   וְדַבֵּק

2. אֱלֹהֵנוּ   לְבֵּנוּ   שְׁמֶךָ   לְאַהֲבָה   אֱלֹהֶיךָ   בְּמִצְוֹתֶיךָ

What word means "Your Torah"? _____.

What word means "our hearts"? _____.

Incognito Words and Root Words

Some Hebrew words and root words change a little. ה, ו and י can drop out of the word.
Circle the word on each line that is built from the word in the colored box.

3. לֵב   וְיַחֵד   (לְבָבֵנוּ)   אֶת   וְדַבֵּק   בְּתוֹרָתֶךָ

4. אוֹר   בְּתוֹרָתֶךָ   וְהָאֵר   לְבָבֵנוּ   וְדַבֵּק

5. צַוֶּה command   לְבָבֵנוּ   וְהָאֵר   לְאַהֲבָה   בְּמִצְוֹתֶיךָ

Review the vocabulary and make your best guess at the meaning of this portion of אַהֲבָה רַבָּה.

לֵב   דֶּבֶק   תּוֹרָה   עֵינַיִם   אוֹר

1

אֶחָד

Take your best guess at the meaning of this text. Your teacher will help you with your translation.

אהב

וְהָאֵר עֵינֵינוּ בְּתוֹרָתֶךָ

וְדַבֵּק לִבֵּנוּ בְּמִצְוֹתֶיךָ

וְיַחֵד לְבָבֵנוּ לְאַהֲבָה

וּלְיִרְאָה אֶת שְׁמֶךָ.

_____

_____

_____

_____

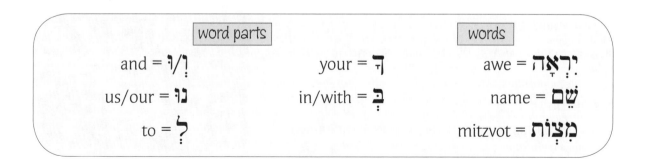

word parts		words
and = וָ/וְ	your = ךָ	awe = יִרְאָה
us/our = נוּ	in/with = בְּ	name = שֵׁם
to = לְ		mitzvot = מִצְוֹת

Two Memories of Sinai

Sometimes different people remember the same event differently. The Jewish people have two different memories of receiving the Torah at Mt. Sinai.

Here is the first memory: The Torah is very demanding. It asks people to do many things that are not easy, and it asks people not to do many things that are not easy to stop yourself from doing.

God went to a lot of different people and asked them to accept the Torah. Each group asked about the Torah, and God repeated one or two of its rules. Each time God described the Torah, the people who heard about it politely said, "No, thank you!" There were things the Torah asked them to do that they did not want to do. There were things the Torah asked them not to do that they did not want to stop doing. Israel was God's last chance. Everyone else had said, "No, thank you!"

The Families-of-Israel were at Mt. Sinai. They said, "No, thank you." This time God was prepared. God lifted up the mountain and held it over their heads. It hung in the air like a huge, open coffin. God said to Israel, "Do you want to accept My Torah, or do you want Me to put the mountain down?"

It was at that moment, with Mt. Sinai hanging over their heads, that the Families-of-Israel said, "We will do it and we will obey it." That is how Israel accepted the Torah.

The second memory is very different. Israel really wanted the Torah. They believed that it would be fun to celebrate all the holidays. They thought that it would be an honor to become God's partner. Just like little kids, Israel jumped up and down and hollered, "Choose me! Pick me!"

God said to Israel, "Why should I pick you? The Torah is really valuable. Who will promise that you will treat it well? Who will guarantee that you will not ruin it?"

Israel said, "Abraham, Sarah, Isaac, Rebekkah, Leah, Rachel, and Jacob will be responsible."

God answered, "Every one of them broke the rules of the Torah at some point and did something wrong. They are not the ones to protect My Torah."

Israel said, "How about the prophets? They all taught Your word."

God answered, "They told you the right things to do, and you usually did not listen to them. If you won't listen to the prophets, how can I make them responsible?"

Finally, Israel had a big conference and said to God, "Our children will be the ones to take responsibility. They promise that they will study the Torah and take it into their hearts. They promise to make the future better."

God thought about it and then said, "The Torah is yours."

As God gave them the Torah, the Families-of-Israel shouted out, "We will do it and we will obey it." That is how Israel accepted the Torah.

From the Midrash

Questions

1. Have you ever felt like you were trapped in the first memory of Mt. Sinai—as if being Jewish is something you are forced to do?
2. Have you ever felt like you were living the second memory, proud and privileged to be Jewish?
3. Why do we need both stories? How can both memories help us to say the אַהֲבָה רַבָּה?

21

שְׁמַע

The שְׁמַע is probably the most important sentence in the whole Torah. It states the single most important Jewish idea—there is only One God.

The שְׁמַע is also a collection of three paragraphs in the Torah that come from three different places and were brought together to be the heart of one part of the morning and evening services. The three-paragraph שְׁמַע was created to solve a problem.

Originally, back in the time of the Temple, the Ten Commandments were recited as part of the Temple service every day. It was a big performance remembering being at Mt. Sinai. People began to take the Ten Commandments too seriously. They began to believe that those were the only important מִצְוֹת. They would say, "I am a good Jew, I do The Big Ten," and not bother with the rest of the 613 מִצְוֹת. The Rabbis of the Talmud knew that they had to make a change.

They found three passages in the Torah that all said כָּל מִצְוֹתַי, "all My commandments." They replaced the Ten Commandments with this new collection of passages.

The שְׁמַע teaches us that God is One. It then makes sure that we live that Oneness at every moment of the day, everywhere we go, with everyone we meet, through everything we do. How can you live the truth that God is One?

22

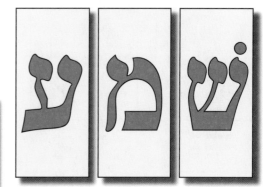

ROOT ANALYSIS

Can you see the three letters שְׁמַע in these words?

לִשְׁמֹעַ   שְׁמַע   שׁוֹמֵעַ

to listen = לִשְׁמֹעַ
listen! (command) = שְׁמַע
listens = שׁוֹמֵעַ

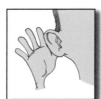

Practice these words and phrases and circle all that contain the root שְׁמַע.

1. אֶחָד   לִשְׁמֹעַ   כָּבוֹד   בָּרְכוּ   הִשְׁתַּמֵּעַ   מַלְכֵי

2. נִשְׁמַע   וָעֶד   כְּמוֹשִׁיעֵנוּ   מַלְכֵּנוּ   יִשְׁמְעוּ   מַה

3. כְּמַלְכֵּנוּ   שׁוֹמֵעַ   אֵין   שְׁמַע   קוֹלֵנוּ   נִשְׁמַע

4. שְׁמַע יִשְׂרָאֵל   מַלְכוּתוֹ   יי אֶחָד   שֵׁם כָּבוֹד

5. בָּרוּךְ שֵׁם כָּבוֹד   לְעוֹלָם וָעֶד   שְׁמַע יִשְׂרָאֵל

6. יי אֱלֹהֵינוּ יי אֶחָד   כְּבוֹד מַלְכוּתוֹ לְעוֹלָם וָעֶד

7. שְׁמַע יִשְׂרָאֵל יי אֱלֹהֵינוּ יי אֶחָד

8. בָּרוּךְ שֵׁם כְּבוֹד מַלְכוּתוֹ לְעוֹלָם וָעֶד

23

Review the vocabulary and make your best guess at the meaning of the שְׁמַע.

כָּבֵד

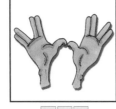

בָּרַךְ

אֶחָד

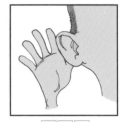

יִשְׂרָאֵל

שְׁמַע

מֶלֶךְ

Take your best guess at the meaning of this text. Your teacher will help you with your translation.

שְׁמַע יִשְׂרָאֵל יי אֱלֹהֵינוּ יי אֶחָד.
בָּרוּךְ שֵׁם כְּבוֹד מַלְכוּתוֹ לְעוֹלָם וָעֶד.

_____

_____

_____

עוֹלָם

words

our God = אֱלֹהֵינוּ

name = שֵׁם

and more = וָעֶד

honor = כָּבוֹד

word parts

us/our = נוּ

His = וֹ   to = לְ

Choreography

When we say the שְׁמַע we do many things to help the words reach our souls and move our hearts.

1. Traditionally, one may stand or sit for the שְׁמַע, but many congregations stand to make it a declaration (like the Pledge of Allegiance).

2. We close our eyes and cover them—so that we are thinking and feeling and not looking around.

3. We make sure that we say every word slowly and clearly, thinking about the meaning.

4. We hold onto the word אֶחָד, making sure that we pronounce the final "ד" so that it will not be mistaken for another word.

The Death of Jacob

All of the שְׁמַע is found in the Torah except for one sentence. The part where we say בָּרוּךְ שֵׁם כְּבוֹד מַלְכוּתוֹ לְעוֹלָם וָעֶד is not in there. In most synagogues (but not in many Reform synagogues) this sentence is whispered every day except Yom Kippur. In the Talmud and the Midrash we find three different stories of the origin of the בָּרוּךְ שֵׁם sentence. Two of them also explain the whisper.

Jacob is in Egypt, and he is old and ready to die. Jacob has a second name—at least some of the time he is called יִשְׂרָאֵל. On his deathbed, Jacob gathers his children and tells them, "I am afraid to die."

They answer, "There is no need to fear death, Father. God loves you."

Jacob says, "I am not afraid of dying—I am afraid of leaving you in Egypt without me. Egypt is a land that believes in many gods. Its people carve statues of people out of sides of mountains and pretend that they are gods. I am afraid that when I am gone, you will forget the one God, the God Who spoke to Abraham and Isaac and me."

His children answer together in loud voices, "שְׁמַע יִשְׂרָאֵל (Listen, Dad), יי אֱלֹהֵינוּ (Adonai is our God), יי אֶחָד (only Adonai)."

With his dying breath Jacob whispers, "בָּרוּךְ הַשֵּׁם (Praised be God!) כְּבוֹד מַלְכוּתוֹ לְעוֹלָם וָעֶד (God's glorious empire will last forever)."

When we say the שְׁמַע and whisper the בָּרוּךְ שֵׁם we are acting out this story.

From the Midrash

Questions
1. How is the way we say the שְׁמַע a kind of performance of this story?
2. What were Israel's children promising him? When do you make the same promise?
3. What was Israel's feeling when he said the בָּרוּךְ שֵׁם (and added it to the שְׁמַע)? When have you felt the same way?
4. What is the "Oneness" in this story?
5. How can remembering this story help you point your heart when you say the שְׁמַע?

וְאָהַבְתָּ

The וְאָהַבְתָּ is:
- part of the first paragraph of the שְׁמַע, or
- the prayer that comes after the שְׁמַע.

It depends how your סִדּוּר is organized.

The וְאָהַבְתָּ comes from the book of Deuteronomy, chapter 6, verse 5. The verse before this one is the sentence that begins שְׁמַע יִשְׂרָאֵל.

The וְאָהַבְתָּ continues the idea that God is our God.

It teaches us that:
- we should love God,
- the way to show our love is by studying and living Torah,
- מִצְוֹת are the way we live Torah,
- there are מִצְוֹת we can do at all times of the day (every day),
- there are מִצְוֹת we can do anywhere and everywhere we go,
- some Jewish things we do help us to remember the מִצְוֹת,
- teaching Torah to our children is a very important מִצְוָה.

Some congregations say three paragraphs of the שְׁמַע in their service, some say only one. Those that say only one take the last line of the third paragraph and put it on the ending of the וְאָהַבְתָּ. This is the part that tells us that by doing the מִצְוֹת we become קָדוֹשׁ, holy.

וְאָהַבְתָּ

.1	שְׁמַע יִשְׂרָאֵל	LISTEN, ISRAEL,
.2	יי אֱלֹהֵינוּ יי אֶחָד.	ADONAI is our God, ADONAI is the ONE (and only) God.
.3	בָּרוּךְ שֵׁם כְּבוֹד מַלְכוּתוֹ	BLESSED be the NAME—that God's HONORED EMPIRE
.4	לְעוֹלָם וָעֶד.	will last FOREVER and ALWAYS.
.5	וְאָהַבְתָּ אֵת יי אֱלֹהֶיךָ	You should LOVE ADONAI your God
.6	בְּכָל־לְבָבְךָ	with all your HEART
.7	וּבְכָל־נַפְשְׁךָ	with all your SOUL
.8	וּבְכָל־מְאֹדֶךָ.	with all your STUFF.
.9	וְהָיוּ הַדְּבָרִים הָאֵלֶּה	And these THINGS that
.10	אֲשֶׁר אָנֹכִי מְצַוְּךָ הַיּוֹם	I make MITZVOT for you today
.11	עַל לְבָבֶךָ.	shall be on your HEART.
.12	וְשִׁנַּנְתָּם לְבָנֶיךָ	You should TEACH them to your children
.13	וְדִבַּרְתָּ בָּם	and you should TALK about them
.14	בְּשִׁבְתְּךָ בְּבֵיתֶךָ	when you SIT at home
.15	וּבְלֶכְתְּךָ בַדֶּרֶךְ	when you are GOING out
.16	וּבְשָׁכְבְּךָ	when you LIE down
.17	וּבְקוּמֶךָ.	and when you get UP.
.18	וּקְשַׁרְתָּם לְאוֹת עַל־יָדֶךָ	And you should TIE them as LETTERS on your HAND
.19	וְהָיוּ לְטֹטָפֹת בֵּין עֵינֶיךָ.	And have them as SYMBOLS between your EYES.

.20 וּכְתַבְתָּם עַל-מְזֻזוֹת בֵּיתֶךָ	And you should WRITE them on the DOORPOSTS of your HOUSE
.21 וּבִשְׁעָרֶיךָ.	and on your GATES.
.22 לְמַעַן תִּזְכְּרוּ	That you will REMEMBER
.23 וַעֲשִׂיתֶם אֶת-כָּל מִצְוֹתָי	and DO all My MITZVOT
.24 וִהְיִיתֶם קְדוֹשִׁים לֵאלֹהֵיכֶם.	and BE HOLY for your God.
.25 אֲנִי יי אֱלֹהֵיכֶם	I am ADONAI, your God,
.26 אֲשֶׁר הוֹצֵאתִי אֶתְכֶם	The One-Who-BROUGHT-you-OUT
.27 מֵאֶרֶץ מִצְרַיִם	from the Land of Egypt
.28 לִהְיוֹת לָכֶם לֵאלֹהִים	to BE your God
.29 אֲנִי יי אֱלֹהֵיכֶם. אֱמֶת.	I am ADONAI your God. FOR SURE.

Review the vocabulary and make your best guess at the meaning of the first part of the וְאָהַבְתָּ.

words parts	words	
and = וְ/וּ	soul = נֶפֶשׁ	before a direct object = אֵת
your = ךָ	stuff = מְאֹד	all = כָּל
in/with = בְּ		

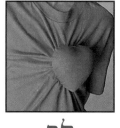

לֵב

אהב

וְאָהַבְתָּ אֵת יי אֱלֹהֶיךָ

בְּכָל־לְבָבְךָ וּבְכָל־נַפְשְׁךָ וּבְכָל־מְאֹדֶךָ.

Take your best guess at the meaning of this text. Your teacher will help you with your translation.

_____

_____

_____

קָמֵץ קָטָן

Sometimes the vowel ◌ָ is pronounced like an וֹ and not an ◌ָ. When that happens, it is called a *kamatz katan*. In this book we will print every ◌ָ *kamatz katan* a little larger than an ordinary ◌ָ, and it will be easier for you to recognize them.

Kamatz katan means "a short *kamatz*." A regular *kamatz* makes an "ah" sound. A *kamatz katan* makes an "awe" sound. According to people who study languages, an "awe" is a short "ah."

There are some very complicated rules for knowing when to say a *kamatz katan*. A lot of words will become familiar because you will use them often.

Here are two words from the prayer וְאָהַבְתָּ that contain a *kamatz katan*.

וּבְשָׁכְבְּךָ   בְּכָל

Phrase Drill

Practice these phrases.

1. שְׁמַע יִשְׂרָאֵל יְיָ אֱלֹהֵינוּ יְיָ אֶחָד   בָּרוּךְ שֵׁם כְּבוֹד מַלְכוּתוֹ

2. וְשִׁנַּנְתָּם לְבָנֶיךָ וְדִבַּרְתָּ בָּם   וְהָיוּ לְטֹטָפֹת בֵּין עֵינֶיךָ

3. יוֹצֵר אוֹר וּבוֹרֵא חֹשֶׁךְ   חֶמְלָה גְדוֹלָה וִיתֵרָה

4. בְּשִׁבְתְּךָ בְּבֵיתֶךָ וּבְלֶכְתְּךָ בַדֶּרֶךְ   וְהָאֵר עֵינֵינוּ בְּתוֹרָתֶךָ

5. אַהֲבָה רַבָּה אֲהַבְתָּנוּ יְיָ אֱלֹהֵינוּ   וּקְשַׁרְתָּם לְאוֹת עַל יָדֶךָ

6. אֲשֶׁר הוֹצֵאתִי אֶתְכֶם מֵאֶרֶץ מִצְרַיִם

7. וּכְתַבְתָּם עַל מְזֻזוֹת בֵּיתֶךָ וּבִשְׁעָרֶיךָ

8. לְמַעַן תִּזְכְּרוּ וַעֲשִׂיתֶם אֶת כָּל מִצְוֹתָי

9. וַהֲבִיאֵנוּ לְשָׁלוֹם מֵאַרְבַּע כַּנְפוֹת הָאָרֶץ

10. הַמֵּאִיר לָאָרֶץ וְלַדָּרִים עָלֶיהָ בְּרַחֲמִים

11. וְתֵן בְּלִבֵּנוּ לְהָבִין וּלְהַשְׂכִּיל לִשְׁמוֹעַ לִלְמֹד וּלְלַמֵּד

12. וְדַבֵּק לִבֵּנוּ בְּמִצְוֹתֶךָ וְיַחֵד לְבָבֵנוּ לְאַהֲבָה וּלְיִרְאָה אֶת שְׁמֶךָ

31

Review the vocabulary and make your best guess at the meaning of another part of the וְאָהַבְתָּ.

הָלַךְ   בַּיִת   יָשַׁב   דִּבֵּר   בָּנִים

דֶּרֶךְ

Take your best guess at the meaning of this text. Your teacher will help you with your translation.

וְשִׁנַּנְתָּם לְבָנֶיךָ וְדִבַּרְתָּ בָּם

בְּשִׁבְתְּךָ בְּבֵיתֶךָ

וּבְלֶכְתְּךָ בַדֶּרֶךְ

וּבְשָׁכְבְּךָ וּבְקוּמֶךָ

שָׁכַב

קוּם

_____

_____

_____

_____

word parts		words
and = וְ/וּ	your = ךָ	teach them = שִׁנַּנְתָּם
to = לְ	in/with = בְּ	them = בָּם

Moses Steals the שֶׁמַע

Moses went up to heaven to get the Torah. All the angels were gathered around him, carrying signs and yelling, "Keep the Torah! Don't let it go!"

Moses took off his *tallit katan,* the little tallit he wore under his robe, and tied it onto his staff. He shouted, "Truce." Four angels came forward to talk to him, Michael, Gavriel, Uzziel, and Raphael. Moses said, "Let me ask three questions. Then you can choose to let me have the Torah, or I will just go home and not bother you anymore."

They said, "We can handle three questions."

Moses asked, "Who here has ever been disrespectful to their parents? Please raise your hand if the answer is 'yes'." Every angel held their hands down.

They said, "We are angels—we don't have parents."

Then Moses asked, "Who has ever stolen something? Please shout out 'Me.'"

The angels were silent. They put their hands over their mouths, and through their fingers they said, "We are angels—we don't steal."

33

Finally Moses asked, "Who here has ever murdered someone? Please take a step forward."

Every angel took a step back, except one, who stood still. All of the angels said, "We're angels—we don't murder."

Then Moses shouted, "Don't you get it? You don't need the Torah—we do. Torah isn't for those who already do what God wants. Torah is for those of us who need to learn how to be more like God in our actions."

The angels agreed. They shouted out, "Give the Torah to Moses," and they carried him around on their shoulders.

Then the one angel who had not moved, the Angel of Death, came to Moses and whispered three words, "*T'shuvah* (repentence), *t'fillah* (prayer) and *tzedakah* (charity). These are the ways to keep me away."

Just before he left heaven, Moses heard music in the background. He realized that Gavriel and some of the other angels were always filling heaven with songs of praise. One of the songs they were singing over and over went,

"בָּרוּךְ שֵׁם כְּבוֹד מַלְכוּתוֹ לְעוֹלָם וָעֶד."

Moses stole the angels' song and brought it back to earth along with the Torah.

We now sing the angels' song, "בָּרוּךְ שֵׁם," as part of the שְׁמַע every day. We whisper it because it was stolen. We say it out loud on Yom Kippur. That is the day by which we have done *t'shuvah, t'fillah* and *tzedakah*. It is the one time when we are not guilty of being disrespectful to parents, of stealing, or of murdering. It is the one time that we are as holy as angels. (Based on a story in the Talmud)

Questions
1. Why do we usually whisper part of the שְׁמַע?
2. Why do we say it out loud on Yom Kippur?
3. This story teaches us that we are supposed to live the truth that there is One God by acting the way God wants. What are some of the ways of acting that are on God's list?
4. What is the "Oneness" in this story?
5. How can remembering this story help you point your heart when you say the שְׁמַע?

מִי-כָמֹכָה

The מִי-כָמֹכָה is:

• a sentence out of a poem in the Torah,

• part of the song that the families-of-Israel sang when they crossed the Reed Sea,

• part of the בְּרָכָה that comes after the שְׁמַע in both the morning and the evening,

• a reminder that God has helped us and will continue to help us.

When the Families-of-Israel escaped from Egypt, the Egyptians chased them and caught up with them at the Reed Sea. (Reed Sea is what the Hebrew actually says. "Red" Sea is a typo.) God worked a miracle and the sea divided so that Israel crossed it safely on dry land. When the Egyptians tried to follow, the sea closed up, and they drowned. Once they were safely on the other side (or maybe even before) the Families-of-Israel burst into song. The song they sang, the Song of the Sea, includes the מִי-כָמֹכָה.

The third prayer connected to the שְׁמַע, the one that comes after the שְׁמַע, is called the גְּאֻלָה, which means "redemption". Redemption is a combination of rescuing and setting free. God redeemed us from Egyptian slavery. That is why this בְּרָכָה ends by saying בָּרוּךְ אַתָּה יי גָּאַל יִשְׂרָאֵל.

גְּאֻלָּה

Moses and the Families-of-Israel	מֹשֶׁה וּבְנֵי יִשְׂרָאֵל .1
responded to You in very happy song,	לְךָ עָנוּ שִׁירָה בְּשִׂמְחָה רַבָּה, .2
and they all said:	וְאָמְרוּ כֻלָּם: .3
Which of the other (false) gods is like You, ADONAI	מִי־כָמֹכָה בָּאֵלִים יְיָ, .4
Who is like You, GLORIOUS in holiness	מִי כָּמֹכָה נֶאְדָּר בַּקֹּדֶשׁ, .5
AWESOME in praises, DOING miracles?	נוֹרָא תְהִלֹּת עֹשֵׂה פֶלֶא. .6
With a new song	שִׁירָה חֲדָשָׁה .7
The REDEEMED proclaimed Your name	שִׁבְּחוּ גְאוּלִים לְשִׁמְךָ .8
on the sea shore.	עַל שְׂפַת הַיָּם, .9
Together all of them gave thanks and praised Your Empire	יַחַד כֻּלָּם הוֹדוּ וְהִמְלִיכוּ .10
by saying:	וְאָמְרוּ: .11
ADONAI will rule forever and ever.	יְיָ יִמְלֹךְ לְעֹלָם וָעֶד. .12
Rock of Israel,	צוּר יִשְׂרָאֵל .13
Arise in help of Israel	קוּמָה בְּעֶזְרַת יִשְׂרָאֵל, .14
and set (us) free, as You promised	וּפְדֵה כִנְאֻמֶךָ .15
to JUDAH and ISRAEL,	יְהוּדָה וְיִשְׂרָאֵל. .16
our REDEEMER,	גֹּאֲלֵנוּ .17
God's name is ADONAI of Hosts, the Holy One is Israel.	יְיָ צְבָאוֹת שְׁמוֹ קְדוֹשׁ יִשְׂרָאֵל. .18
BLESSED be You, ADONAI	בָּרוּךְ אַתָּה יְיָ .19
The ONE-Who-REDEEMED Israel.	גָּאַל יִשְׂרָאֵל. .20

Review the vocabulary and make your best guess at the meaning of the beginning of the מִי־כָמֹכָה.

Your teacher will help you with your translation.

מִי־כָמֹכָה בָּאֵלִים יי

מִי כָּמֹכָה נֶאְדָּר בַּקֹּדֶשׁ

נוֹרָא תְהִלֹּת עֹשֵׂה פֶלֶא

My best guess at the meaning of this prayer is:

_____

_____

_____

_____

_____

words

awesome = נוֹרָא

praises = תְּהִלֹּת

do/make = עֹשֵׂה

wonder = פֶלֶא

who = מִי

is like = כְּמוֹ

gods = אֵלִים

splendid = נֶאְדָּר

holy = קֹדֶשׁ

word parts

your = ךָ

in/with = בְּ/בַ/בָ

37

The Dagesh

A. Name these Hebrew letters: פ פ כ כ ב ב

B. The dot found inside the letters פ, כ and ב is called a *dagesh*.

What does the *dagesh* do to these letters? _____

C. The *dagesh* can also be found in many other Hebrew letters, but it doesn't change the way the other letters are pronounced.

Circle the letters whose sounds are changed by the dagesh:

1. ד ל מ ג ב ה שׁ פּ ס ק

2. זּ כ צ יּ תּ ט נ שׂ ל ב

Recite these words and phrases from the מִי־כָמֹכָה.

1. פֶּלֶא   כָּמֹכָה   קָיָם   נָעִים   עֹשֵׂה   בָּאֵלִים   אֱמֶת

2. לְעוֹלָם   מִי   תְּהִלֹּת   אָהוּב   יִמְלֹךְ   נוֹרָא   נֶאְדָּר

3. וְנוֹרָא   בַּקֹּדֶשׁ   יַצִּיב   חָבִיב   תְּהִלֹּת   נֶאֱמָן   וָעֶד

4. כָּמֹכָה   נֶחְמָד   נֶאֱמָן   אַדִּיר   מְתֻקָּן   כָּמֹכָה

5. נוֹרָא תְּהִלֹּת עֹשֵׂה פֶּלֶא   מִי כָמֹכָה נֶאְדָּר בַּקֹּדֶשׁ

6. יי יִמְלֹךְ לְעֹלָם וָעֶד   מִי־כָמֹכָה בָּאֵלִים יי

Review the vocabulary and make your best guess at the meaning of another part of the מִי־כָמֹכָה.

מֶלֶךְ

Take your best guess at the meaning of this text. Your teacher will help you with your translation.

יי יִמְלֹךְ לְעֹלָם וָעֶד.

My best guess at the meaning of this prayer is:

_____

_____

_____

עוֹלָם

words	word parts
and more = וָעֶד	to = לְ

How to Dance the גְּאֻלָּה

It is a tradition to connect the end of the גְּאֻלָּה directly, without a pause, to the עֲמִידָה, the chain of prayers that follows. The last sentence of the גְּאֻלָּה includes the word קוּמָה at the beginning. קוּמָה means "rise up." It is a tradition to rise up when you say the word קוּמָה and remain standing for the עֲמִידָה that follows.

39

Nahshon's Leap of Faith

Here is one of many stories about the first time the מִי־כָמֹכָה was said.

Israel was trapped at the banks of the Reed Sea. The Egyptian army was coming, and there was nowhere to run. Everyone was in a panic. No one knew how to swim well enough. It was a mob scene. God was supposed to rescue them, but nothing was happening. Nahshon ben Aminadav, from the tribe of Judah, figured out the answer. He found himself a little space, backed up, and took a running leap toward the sea. He jumped way out into the water, but he never got wet. When his toe got to a place where it should have touched the water, the sea divided under him and he landed on dry land. Israel could then march forward into the dry sea bed. *(From the Midrash)*

Questions

1. What did Nahshon figure out about what God wants from us?
2. What is the lesson of this midrash?
3. How can remembering the story of Nahshon help us to point our hearts when we say the מִי־כָמֹכָה?

אֲדֹנָי שְׂפָתַי תִּפְתָּח

These words are a warm-up. They come from a poem written by King David (*Psalms* 51.17). It came from a moment when King David was having a lot of trouble knowing how to pray. Just as David spoke them to God as a way of beginning his prayer, we do the same.

Levi Yitzhak of Berdichev explained that in the days when the עֲמִידָה was first created, these words were not part of it. He taught, "In those days, people knew how to point their hearts and feel close to God." In our day, אֲדֹנָי שְׂפָתַי תִּפְתָּח has been added as a prayer to get us ready to pray.

When God created Adam and Eve, God breathed into them the spirit of speech (*Targum*, Gen. 2.7). Words are the things that make people different from animals. Words are our special gift. This prayer takes us back to the first people and asks God to help us use our words.

The Rabbis teach that two things make it hard for us to sincerely pray the עֲמִידָה:

• We don't feel that we are good enough to deserve God's help. We are afraid that things we have done wrong will bother God too much. We are afraid that God won't help us.

• We are afraid to admit that we need help. To pray the עֲמִידָה we have to admit that we have problems we cannot fix on our own.

41

Can you see the three letters פתח in these words?

תִּפְתַּח פּוֹתֵחַ פִּתְחוּ

You will open = תִּפְתַּח

open = פּוֹתֵחַ

Open! = פִּתְחוּ

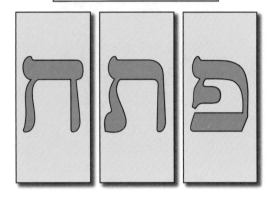

Practice these phrases and circle all the words that contain the root פתח.

---

1. פִּתְחוּ לִי שַׁעֲרֵי צֶדֶק   פּוֹתֵחַ אֶת יָדֶךָ

---

2. אֲדֹנָי שְׂפָתַי תִּפְתָּח   אֲנִי־עַבְדְּךָ בֶּן־אֲמָתֶךָ פִּתַּחְתָּ לְמוֹסֵרָי

Can you see the three letters נגד in these words? Notice that with this root, the נ falls out.

הַגָּדָה מַגִּיד יַגִּיד

he will tell = יַגִּיד

he tells/the telling = מַגִּיד

Haggadah = הַגָּדָה

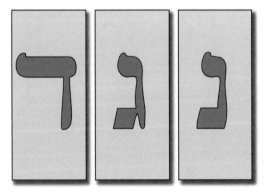

Practice these words and circle all the words that contain the root נגד.

---

3. שְׂפָתַי לְהַגִּיד אֲדֹנָי הַגָּדָה הַגֵּד יַגִּיד

---

4. תִּפְתַּח וּפִי הַגִּיד תְּהִלָּתֶךָ מַגִּיד חֲסָדִים

Can you see the three letters הלל in these words?

Sometimes one of the ל letters falls out.

ROOT ANALYSIS

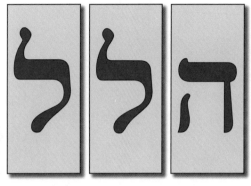

הַלֵּל   תְּהִלָּה   הַלְלוּיָהּ

prayers of praise (psalms) = הַלֵּל

praise = תְּהִלָּה

Praise the Eternal! = הַלְלוּיָהּ

Practice these phrases and circle all the words that contain the root הלל.

1. הַלְלוּ   עַבְדֵי   וְכִנּוֹר   הַנְּשָׁמָה   תְּהַלֵּל   הַלְלוּהוּ

2. הַלְלוּהוּ בְּתֵקַע שׁוֹפָר   וְצִוָּנוּ לִקְרֹא אֶת־הַהַלֵּל

TRANSLATION

Review the vocabulary and make your best guess at the introduction to the עֲמִידָה.

הלל

נ ג ד

פֶּה

פתח

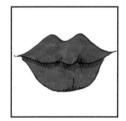
שְׂפָתַיִם

אֲדֹנָי שְׂפָתַי תִּפְתָּח וּפִי יַגִּיד תְּהִלָּתֶךָ

Word Parts	Word
and = וּ	God = אֲדֹנָי
your = ךָ	

_____

_____

King David
Messed Up
Big Time

It was the worst moment in King David's life (so far). It started one day when he went out on the roof of the palace and saw a really beautiful woman sunbathing. Immediately he fell in love with her. It didn't matter that she was married to someone else. David had to be with her even though it was wrong. He could not get her out of his head. This was a moment when "I want it" was stronger than "I know this is wrong." David chose the wrong thing.

The woman's name was Batsheva, and her husband was one of David's soldiers. Even though she was married, David started spending time with her. Soon he had to have her for his own. David wrote to one of his generals. He had Batsheva's husband put in the lead in every battle—in the place with the most danger. When he was killed, David took Batsheva as a wife.

Nathan was a prophet in David's court. One day he came to David with a story about a rich man with many sheep who stole a poor man's only sheep. David listened and felt bad. He said, "The rich man deserves to die." Nathan pointed to David and said, "You are that man." Then he said, "God is now very angry with you."

David suddenly realized how wrong he had been. He was really sorry. There was no way that he could bring Batsheva's husband back and make things right. He didn't know how to fix things.

He also was afraid that God would never forgive him. There was now a huge space between him and God—a big black hole. It was then that he sat down and wrote a poem, a prayer to God.

David began:

אֲדֹנָי שְׂפָתַי תִּפְתָּח וּפִי יַגִּיד תְּהִלָּתֶךָ.

He said, "God, I don't know how to begin. Words will not come. I want to talk to You, but I don't know what to say. I don't feel worthy." His prayer began, "Eternal, if You will open my lips and help me begin—then my tongue will find a way to pray to You." We all have times when we feel like David. (*Midrash Tehillim 51; Bet Yosef on Tur 111-112*)

Questions

1. Why was it hard for David to pray to God when it was something he used to do every day?
2. Why did David write a prayer that asked for God's help in praying?
3. How does knowing this story help you to know how to get ready to pray the עֲמִידָה?

45

אָבוֹת וְאִמָּהוֹת

The אָבוֹת וְאִמָּהוֹת is the first prayer in the עֲמִידָה. Rabbi Simlai taught in the Talmud, "One must always start the עֲמִידָה with praise of God before one asks anything of God" (*Brakhot* 32a).

- The אָבוֹת וְאִמָּהוֹת is the first of three "praise" בְּרָכוֹת that begin the עֲמִידָה.

- The big idea of this prayer is זְכוּת אָבוֹת (the merit of our ancestors). This means that we ask God to take care of us because our ancestors were good people who had good relationships with God.

- The Rabbis who organized the סִדּוּר explained their choice of the אָבוֹת וְאִמָּהוֹת as the first prayer because of a Torah story about Moses.

When Israel sinned with the Golden Calf, God was ready to destroy them. Moses stood and prayed to the Holy One to try to change God's mind. None of his prayers worked until he said: "Do it for the sake of Abraham, Isaac, and Israel your servants." It was those words that got God to forgive Israel. Therefore, we begin our עֲמִידָה with that same reminder to God (*Mehilta, Bo* 13.3; *Shabbat* 30a).

Originally, this prayer was just about the אָבוֹת, the "fathers," אַבְרָהָם, יִצְחָק, and יַעֲקֹב. Like many things in Judaism, it was "man" centered. Today many synagogues have added the אִמָּהוֹת, the mothers, שָׂרָה, רִבְקָה, לֵאָה and רָחֵל. This came as part of a growing understanding that all of us need women's stories, too.

46

אָבוֹת וְאִמָּהוֹת

Blessed be You, ADONAI	בָּרוּךְ אַתָּה יי .1
our God and God of our FATHERS & our MOTHERS	אֱלֹהֵינוּ וֵאלֹהֵי אֲבוֹתֵינוּ וְאִמּוֹתֵינוּ. .2
God of ABRAHAM	אֱלֹהֵי אַבְרָהָם .3
God of ISAAC	אֱלֹהֵי יִצְחָק .4
and God of JACOB.	וֵאלֹהֵי יַעֲקֹב. .5
God of SARAH	אֱלֹהֵי שָׂרָה .6
God of REBEKKAH	אֱלֹהֵי רִבְקָה .7
God of LEAH	אֱלֹהֵי רָחֵל .8
and God of RACHEL	וֵאלֹהֵי לֵאָה. .9
The GOD, The GREAT One, The HERO, THE AWESOME One	הָאֵל הַגָּדוֹל הַגִּבּוֹר וְהַנּוֹרָא .10
God on High	אֵל עֶלְיוֹן .11
The ONE-Who-NURSES with GOOD KINDNESS	גּוֹמֵל חֲסָדִים טוֹבִים .12
and the ONE-Who-OWNS everything	וְקוֹנֵה הַכֹּל .13
and the ONE-Who-REMEMBERS the kindness of the Parents,	וְזוֹכֵר חַסְדֵי אָבוֹת וְאִמָּהוֹת .14
and brings a REDEMEER/REDEMPTION	וּמֵבִיא גּוֹאֵל/גְּאוּלָה .15
to their children's children	לִבְנֵי בְנֵיהֶם .16
for the sake of God's NAME.	לְמַעַן שְׁמוֹ בְּאַהֲבָה. .17
RULER, HELPER—and SAVIOR and PROTECTOR.	מֶלֶךְ עוֹזֵר וּמוֹשִׁיעַ וּמָגֵן. .18
Blessed be You, ADONAI	בָּרוּךְ אַתָּה יי .19
The ONE-Who-PROTECTS Abraham	מָגֵן אַבְרָהָם .20
and The ONE-Who HELPS Sarah/REMEMBERS Sarah.	וְעֶזְרַת שָׂרָה/וּפֹקֵד שָׂרָה. .21

Traditional version/Reform and Reconstructionist version

How to Dance the עֲמִידָה

We begin the עֲמִידָה by standing up, facing Jerusalem, taking three steps forward, and then standing with our feet together. Some of the prayers we may sing together, but if we don't, they are said in a whisper, loud enough to be heard by your own ears but by no one else.

Each of these "dance steps" has us acting out a different story.

When we **stand up** we are like Abraham. Abraham was the first person to figure out that there was only one God. In the Talmud (*Brakhot* 26b) we learn that he invented the morning service. He got up every morning and stood before the God he knew was there.

When we **face Jerusalem** we are like King Solomon (*1 Kings* 8.44-48) creating a house where God can be our neighbor. When we face toward Jerusalem we are recreating our pilgrimage toward the Temple where sacrifices united all Jews. Now, three times a day, the עֲמִידָה creates the same connections.

When we take **three steps forward** we are like Moses. Moses went up Mount Sinai to come close to God. The Torah tells us that there was "darkness, a cloud, and thick fog" between Moses and the top of the mountain (*Deut.* 4.11). God was hidden, and Moses had to work to get close. The three steps are our "darkness, cloud, and fog." They remind us that we, too, have to work to feel close to God. (Often people take three steps back in order to take three steps forward.)

The Baal Shem Tov explained these three steps by saying, "When a child is learning to walk, a parent takes three steps back and stands with open arms, giving the child room to learn. Like a parent, God takes three steps back from us, to give us the room we need. To begin the עֲמִידָה we take those three steps back to God."

When we **whisper** we are like Hannah. Hannah was a woman who needed God's help. She whispered when she prayed, and God answered her. In the Talmud we are taught, "We whisper to remind ourselves that God is always close. We have no need to yell" (*Sotah* 32b; *Brakhot* 31a).

When we **stand with our feet together** we are like angels. In the Bible we learn that angels who are close to God's throne stand with their feet together (*Ezekiel* 1.7). When we ask God for the things we need, we stand like one of those angels.

Who or what do you feel like when you stand and begin the עֲמִידָה?

48

Review the vocabulary and make your best guess at the meaning of the opening to אָבוֹת וְאִמָּהוֹת.

יִצְחָק

אַבְרָהָם

אֵם

אָב

אַתָּה

בָּרוּךְ

יַעֲקֹב

בָּרוּךְ אַתָּה יי אֱלֹהֵינוּ וֵאלֹהֵי אֲבוֹתֵינוּ וְאִמּוֹתֵינוּ

_____

אֱלֹהֵי אַבְרָהָם אֱלֹהֵי יִצְחָק וֵאלֹהֵי יַעֲקֹב

_____

שָׂרָה

אֱלֹהֵי שָׂרָה אֱלֹהֵי רִבְקָה אֱלֹהֵי רָחֵל וֵאלֹהֵי לֵאָה

_____

_____

רִבְקָה

Choreography

We bend our knees and bow on the opening and closing of this בְּרָכָה.

- *Sefer Abudarham*, a major commentary on the סִדּוּר, teaches that we are supposed to bend like a lulav, separating each of the joints in our spine.

- Bowing symbolizes a sense of humility. Arrogance keeps people from connecting. Egotism creates distance between you and God (*Brakhot* 34a).

רָחֵל

- The שֻׁלְחָן עָרוּךְ (*Orakh Hayyim* 113.7) teaches we should bend our whole body as if we were falling down, but stand up straight before we reach God's name (יי). This reminds us that God is the One WQho keeps us from falling.

What is your best reason for bowing at the beginning of the אָבוֹת וְאִמָּהוֹת?

לֵאָה

49

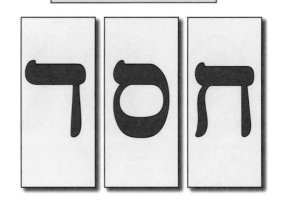

Can you see the three letters חסד in these words?

חֶסֶד   חַסְדֵי   חֲסָדִים

חֶסֶד = kindness

חַסְדֵי = kindness of

גְּמִילוּת חֲסָדִים = acts of kindness

Practice these words and circle all the words that contain the root חסד.

1. גְּמִילוּת   חֲסָדִים   אֲבוֹתֵינוּ   אֵל   עֶלְיוֹן   חֶסֶד

2. זוֹכֵר   חַסְדֵי   אָבוֹת   אִמָּהוֹת   גָּדוֹל   גִּבּוֹר   הַכֹּל

Can you see the three letters זכר in these words?

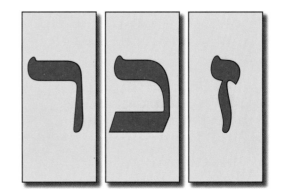

זוֹכֵר   זָכְרֵנוּ   זִכָּרוֹן

זוֹכֵר = remembers

זָכְרֵנוּ = remember us

זִכָּרוֹן = rembrance

Practice these phrases and circle all the words that contain the root זכר.

3. זֵכֶר לִיצִיאַת מִצְרַיִם   לְמַעַן תִּזְכְּרוּ וַעֲשִׂיתֶם

4. בָּרוּךְ אַתָּה יי זוֹכֵר הַבְּרִית   זָכְרֵנוּ לְחַיִּים מֶלֶךְ חָפֵץ בַּחַיִּים

Review the vocabulary and make your best guess at the meaning of another part of אָבוֹת וְאִמָּהוֹת.

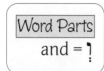

Word Parts
and = וְ

אֵם

אָב

חֶסֶד

זֵכֶר

Your teacher will help you with your translation.

וְזוֹכֵר חַסְדֵי אָבוֹת וְאִמָּהוֹת

Practice, Practice and More Practice

Practice these phrases from the אָבוֹת וְאִמָּהוֹת.

גּוֹמֵל חֲסָדִים טוֹבִים	1. אֱלֹהֵי לֵאָה וֵאלֹהֵי רָחֵל
הָאֵל הַגָּדוֹל הַגִּבּוֹר וְהַנּוֹרָא	2. מֶלֶךְ עוֹזֵר וּמוֹשִׁיעַ וּמָגֵן
אֱלֹהֵינוּ וֵאלֹהֵי אֲבוֹתֵינוּ	3. וְזוֹכֵר חַסְדֵי אָבוֹת וְאִמָּהוֹת
וּמֵבִיא גוֹאֵל לִבְנֵי בְנֵיהֶם	4. וּמֵבִיא גְאוּלָה לִבְנֵי בְנֵיהֶם
	5. בָּרוּךְ אַתָּה יי מָגֵן אַבְרָהָם וּפֹקֵד שָׂרָה
	6. בָּרוּךְ אַתָּה יי מָגֵן אַבְרָהָם וְעֶזְרַת שָׂרָה

Review the vocabulary and make your best guess at the meaning of another part of אָבוֹת וְאִמָּהוֹת.

Word Parts	Words
and = וְ	help = עוֹזֵר
	save = מוֹשִׁיעַ

Your teacher will help you with your translation.

מֶלֶךְ

מָגֵן

מֶלֶךְ עוֹזֵר וּמוֹשִׁיעַ וּמָגֵן.

_____

_____

Shield of Abraham

This is a midrash. Once Abram (who would grow up to become Abraham) discovered that there was only one God, he could not stop spreading the news. His father, Tera<u>h</u>, was an idol maker. Abram worked hard to convince his father's customers that the idols they wanted to buy were of no use.

A powerful man came in and asked for a powerful idol. Abram asked, "How old are you?" The man answered, "I have lived seventy years." Abram asked him, "Then why do you want to bow down before a piece of stone that was carved a few days ago?" The man left.

One day Abram smashed all the idols in his father's store except for one. He put a stick in that idol's hand and told his father, "This idol got in a fight with the other idols and broke them." Terah yelled at his own son, "Are you making fun of me? They are stone—they cannot do anything!" Abram answered, "Father, learn from your own words."

Terah took his son and handed him over to Nimrod, the wicked local king. Nimrod challenged him, "Don't you know that I am god, the Ruler of the Universe." Abram said to him, "Then tomorrow please make the sun rise in the west and set in the east." Nimrod stared at him with anger. Abram then said to him, "You are no god. You are just the son of Cush. You could not keep your father from dying—and eventually you will die, too."

Nimrod had Abram taken away. He was put to work as a slave. The project Abram was working on was the Tower of Babel. This was Nimrod's attempt to reach heaven. Workers on the tower were trained to care more about the bricks than about other workers. Abram started a slave revolt. He taught everyone that there was only One God, that people should care about each other, and that no tower could reach God. Eventually God mixed up the languages of the workers and Abram escaped.

Abram went back home and continued teaching people that Nimrod was not god, because there was only One God. Nimrod had him arrested again. He was taken into the center of the city, tied hand and foot, and placed on a huge bonfire. The fire burned and burned but Abram was protected. Nimrod grabbed his sword and his shield. The shield was a triangle with the point at the bottom. It stood for "Everything comes to me." Abram called for a sword and shield. His shield was also a triangle. Its point was at the top and meant "everything comes from God." The two of them began to fight on the bonfire. It was hot. At one point they banged their shields together and the shields fused. Abram pulled back and he now had a shield with six points. Nimrod fled and Abram was safe. That six-pointed shield was first מָגֵן אַבְרָהָם. Only later did it become מָגֵן דָּוִד. At that moment the angels sang "בָּרוּךְ אַתָּה יי מָגֵן אַבְרָהָם".

(Gen. R. 38.13; P.R.E. 24; Shlomo Carlebach and other sources)

Questions

1. What things do we learn about Abram from this story? When have you been like him?
2. What do we learn about מָגֵן אַבְרָהָם from this story?
3. How can knowing this story help you know where to point your heart when you say the אָבוֹת אִמָּהוֹת?

Sarah's Tent

Sarah had a tent of her own. Every time that the family made camp, Sarah's tent was set up first. Abraham taught men about the One God. Sarah was the women's teacher. Abraham's tent had doors on all four sides so that everyone who was looking for hospitality could easily find their way in. Sarah's tent was where Shabbat was created. Every week Sarah baked _hallah_. Every week Sarah lighted Shabbat candles. The smell of the _hallah_ lasted from week to week. It was always in the tent. The Shabbat lights burned from one Shabbat until the next set were kindled. The tent always smelled of _hallah_. It was always a place of light.

The _Shekhinah_ is the part of God that gets close to people. It is the part that can be our neighbor. God was comfortable with Sarah and her tent. God liked the smell and the light and the peace of Shabbat. The *Shekhinah* would come down in a cloud and rest on Sarah's tent.

When Sarah died, her tent grew dark; the smell of <u>hallah</u> began to fade. Isaac was sad. He refused to see anyone. Abraham sent his servant back to "Padan Aram," the old country, to find a wife for Isaac. The servant picked Rebekkah. When Rebekkah rode into camp, she and Isaac saw each other and fell immediately in love. He took her into his mother's tent. She baked <u>hallah</u> and then lit Shabbat candles. The tent smelled of <u>hallah</u> again. The tent was filled with light again. The *Shekhinah* came back. Isaac finally found comfort after his mother's death.

Years passed. God was hiding in the seventh heaven and crying. Israel had rejected the commandments. They had made a golden calf. All God's dreams were shattered like the tablets. God needed a way to start over. God needed a new beginning. Then God remembered Sarah's tent. God told Moses to have Israel built a tent and to place within it twelve loaves of braided bread and a light that never went out. The tent would always smell like <u>hallah</u>. It would always be a place of light (this was the Mishkan—Tabernacle). God promised that God would come down and be a neighbor just as God had at Sarah's tent (*Gen. R.* 60.16).

Questions
1. What does this story teach us about Sarah?
2. When have you been like her?
3. How can knowing this story help you to know where to point your heart when you say the אָבוֹת וְאִמָּהוֹת?

גְּבוּרוֹת

The גְּבוּרוֹת is:

- the second of the three praise בְּרָכוֹת that begin the עֲמִידָה.
- a prayer that the Talmud names two different ways.
  - called the גְּבוּרוֹת (the "power" prayer) (*Megillah* 17b). That makes it a prayer that talks about God's power through describing some of the good things that God does for people.
  - also called מְחַיֵּה הַמֵּתִים (The One Who-Gives-Life-to-the-Dead) (*Brakhot* 33a). It is a prayer that traditionally centers on the idea that God is stronger than death.

The גְּבוּרוֹת is a place where some modern Jews have changed the סִדּוּר. In a number of סִדּוּרִים the phrase מְחַיֵּה הַמֵּתִים is replaced by מְחַיֵּה הַכֹּל (The One Who-Gives-Life-to-All), or מְחַיֵּה כָּל חַי (The One Who-Gives-and-Renews Life).

This בְּרָכָה is built around the language of Psalm 146. There we are told that God:

- keeps faith forever
- lifts up the fallen
- arranges justice
- feeds the hungry
- sets prisoners free

In the same way that the אָבוֹת וְאִמָּהוֹת, the first prayer in the עֲמִידָה, tells the story of אַבְרָהָם and שָׂרָה and their experiences of God, the גְּבוּרוֹת grows out of stories of יִצְחָק and רִבְקָה (and a יוֹסֵף story, too).

גְּבוּרוֹת

1. You are a HERO forever, my Master:	1. אַתָּה גִבּוֹר לְעוֹלָם אֲדֹנָי
You give LIFE to the dead	2. מְחַיֵּה מֵתִים אַתָּה
You give LIFE to all	מְחַיֵּה הַכֹּל אַתָּה
You are GREAT to bring SALVATION.	3. רַב לְהוֹשִׁיעַ.
The ONE-Who-Returns the wind and Makes the rain come down.	מַשִּׁיב הָרוּחַ וּמוֹרִיד הַגֶּשֶׁם.
Cultivating LIFE in kindness	4. מְכַלְכֵּל חַיִּים בְּחֶסֶד
Giving LIFE to the dead/.	5. מְחַיֵּה מֵתִים/הַכֹּל/כָּל חַי
Giving LIFE to the dead with much mercy.	6. בְּרַחֲמִים רַבִּים.
The ONE-Who-LIFTS-UP the fallen	7. סוֹמֵךְ נוֹפְלִים
and HEALS the sick	8. וְרוֹפֵא חוֹלִים
and FREES prisoners	9. וּמַתִּיר אֲסוּרִים
and ESTABLISHES faith	10. וּמְקַיֵּם אֱמוּנָתוֹ
with those who sleep in the dust.	11. לִישֵׁנֵי עָפָר.
Who is like You, Master of Strength?	12. מִי כָמוֹךָ בַּעַל גְּבוּרוֹת?
And who has Your Image?	13. וּמִי דוֹמֶה לָּךְ?
RULER of DEATH and LIFE	14. מֶלֶךְ מֵמִית וּמְחַיֶּה
and the ONE-Who-Plants SALVATION.	15. וּמַצְמִיחַ יְשׁוּעָה.
And You are faithful to give LIFE to the dead.	16. וְנֶאֱמָן אַתָּה לְהַחֲיוֹת מֵתִים.
Blessed be You, ADONAI.	17. בָּרוּךְ אַתָּה יי
The One-Who-Gives LIFE to the dead.	18. מְחַיֵּה הַמֵּתִים/הַכֹּל/כָּל חַי.

Traditional/Reform/Reconstructionist

Review the vocabulary and make your best guess at the meaning of the opening of the גְבוּרוֹת.

words

Adonai = אֲדֹנָי

life = חַי

dead = מֵת

all = כֹּל

great = רַב

save = [ישע]

word parts

the = הַ

to = לְ

עוֹלָם   גִּבּוֹר   אַתָּה

אַתָּה גִּבּוֹר לְעוֹלָם אֲדֹנָי מְחַיֵּה

_____

מֵתִים אַתָּה

_____

הַכֹּל אַתָּה

_____

רַב לְהוֹשִׁיעַ.

_____

Background on the Different Versions

תְּחִיַּת הַמֵּתִים (Resurrection of the Dead) is a belief that at some time in the future God will regather our bodies from the soil and place our souls back in them, giving us a second chance to live.

1. Maimonides was a famous Jewish philosopher who wrote a list of thirteen things that every Jew was supposed to believe. Number thirteen has to do with the phrase מְחַיֶּה הַמֵּתִים—giving life to the dead. "I believe with complete faith that there will be a resurrection of the dead whenever the Creator wishes it...For Your salvation, Eternal, do I wait."

2. In 1869 a conference of Reform rabbis voted on a resolution and decided "The belief in bodily resurrection has no religious foundation and the doctrine of immortality refers to the afterexistence of the soul alone." The Reform Movement adopted מְחַיֶּה הַכֹּל—giving life to all. Some services in recent Reform סִדּוּרִים have gone back to the original.

3. The Conservative Movement has left the words unchanged but often suggests different understandings. In a book called *Higher and Higher*, Steven M. Brown provides a list of alternative understandings: • People live on in the memories of others. • People's good works live on after them. • The soul is resurrected and comes back in another body. • People can be revived spiritually so life takes on new meaning. • People recuperate after severe illness. • Someone pronounced dead can be revived by C.P.R.

LESSON 15

Practice these phrases from the גְּבוּרוֹת.

1. וּמְקַיֵּם אֱמוּנָתוֹ לִישֵׁנֵי עָפָר   מְחַיֵּה הַכֹּל בְּרַחֲמִים רַבִּים

2. מִי כָמוֹךָ בַּעַל גְּבוּרוֹת   מְחַיֵּה כָּל חַי

3. מֶלֶךְ מֵמִית וּמְחַיֶּה   וּמַצְמִיחַ יְשׁוּעָה   וּמִי דוֹמֶה לָּךְ

4. סוֹמֵךְ נוֹפְלִים   וְרוֹפֵא חוֹלִים   וּמַתִּיר אֲסוּרִים

5. מְכַלְכֵּל חַיִּים בְּחֶסֶד   מְחַיֵּה הַכֹּל בְּרַחֲמִים רַבִּים

6. אַתָּה גִּבּוֹר לְעוֹלָם אֲדֹנָי   מְחַיֵּה מֵתִים אַתָּה רַב לְהוֹשִׁיעַ

7. וְנֶאֱמָן אַתָּה לְהַחֲיוֹת הַכֹּל   בָּרוּךְ אַתָּה יי מְחַיֵּה הַמֵּתִים

Phrase Detective

Look at these four phrases from the גְּבוּרוֹת. What do all four phrases have in common?

8. אַתָּה גִּבּוֹר לְעוֹלָם אֲדֹנָי מְחַיֵּה מֵתִים אַתָּה רַב לְהוֹשִׁיעַ

9. מְכַלְכֵּל חַיִּים בְּחֶסֶד מְחַיֵּה כָּל חַי בְּרַחֲמִים רַבִּים

10. מֶלֶךְ מֵמִית וּמְחַיֶּה וּמַצְמִיחַ יְשׁוּעָה

11. וְנֶאֱמָן אַתָּה לְהַחֲיוֹת מֵתִים   בָּרוּךְ אַתָּה יי מְחַיֵּה הַכֹּל

Review the vocabulary and make your best guess at the meaning of this part of the גְּבוּרוֹת.

אָסוּר

חוֹלֶה

רוֹפֵא

נוֹפֵל

סוֹמֵךְ

יָשֵׁן

Take your best guess at the meaning of this text. Your teacher will help you with your translation.

סוֹמֵךְ נוֹפְלִים וְרוֹפֵא חוֹלִים וּמַתִּיר אֲסוּרִים
וּמְקַיֵּם אֱמוּנָתוֹ לִישֵׁנֵי עָפָר

עָפָר

_____

_____

_____

_____

words		
free = מַתִּיר	establish = מְקַיֵּם	God's faith = אֱמוּנָתוֹ

Giving Life to the Dead

This is the way that one midrash retells the hardest story in the Torah.

God told Abraham to bring his son up "as an offering." Abraham tried some delaying tactics but they did not work.

He got up the next morning and saddled a donkey. The donkey was one of the miraculous things that God created in the last hour before the first Shabbat. This was the same donkey that Moses would use to take his wife and sons to Egypt. This was also the donkey that the Messiah will use to ride into Jerusalem.

Three days later they reached the mountain. They saw a pillar of fire rising from the mountain top—a clear indication that the שְׁכִינָה, the neighborly part of God, was waiting there. They went up to the top of the mountain. God showed them a place where an altar had been built. It was where Cain and Abel had offered their sacrifices. It was where Noah and his family had offered sacrifices. Abraham rebuilt this altar. Later Solomon would build the Temple here. Later the Jewish People would build an altar on this spot, offer sacrifices, and ask to be forgiven.

Isaac said to his father, "Please bind me hand and foot so that I do not flinch. Help me to follow the command to 'Honor your father.'" God watched as Abraham was binding with all his heart and Isaac was bound with all his heart. The angels cried.

Abraham picked up the knife to kill his son. He touched the blade to Isaac's neck, and Isaac's soul fled. He was as good as dead. When the angels cried to Abraham, "Lay not your hands upon the boy," Isaac's soul returned. He stood up and said, "בָּרוּךְ אַתָּה יי מְחַיֶּה הַמֵּתִים." He said it not only about himself, but because he now understood that all people will have an afterlife.

Abraham sacrificed a ram on this altar and not his son. This ram was another one of the miraculous things created in the last hour before the first Shabbat. God turned the ram into a promise for a better future. Its ashes were used to mark the altar in the Temple. Its tendons would become the strings on King David's harp. Its skin would become Elijah's belt. Its horns became the *shofrot* that would announce the coming of the Messiah. The angels sang, "בָּרוּךְ אַתָּה יי מְחַיֶּה הַמֵּתִים" (*Pirkei d'Rabbi Eliezer* 31).

Questions

1. What did Isaac learn about God in this story?
2. How is this a story about תְּחִיַּת הַמֵּתִים?
3. How were the things made out of the ram signs of a better future?
4. How does this story help you know where to point your heart when you say the גְּבוּרוֹת?
5. If you belong to a synagogue that says מְחַיֶּה הַכֹּל, what can you learn about the גְּבוּרוֹת from this story?

קְדוּשָׁה

The קְדוּשָׁה is understood to be the angels' prayer. For some Jews, angels are very real. For other Jews angels are a metaphor—a way of describing a special state of holiness, a special sense of closeness to God.

The קְדוּשָׁה is built out of stories about Isaiah, Ezekiel, and Jacob.

The קְדוּשָׁה is:

• the third praise בְּרָכָה that begins the עֲמִידָה.

• said silently in some congregations and then sometimes repeated aloud. In other settings it is only said aloud by the congregation.

• a dialogue, a back-and-forth singing or reading, between the congregation and the service leader.

• a prayer about holiness.

There is a מִצְוָה called קְדוּש הַשֵׁם. It means "making God's name holy," and that means giving God a great reputation. Sometimes קְדוּש הַשֵׁם means martyrdom. That is dying for a good cause because God's rules and God's values are sometimes worth giving up one's life for. But קְדוּש הַשֵׁם can also mean living in such a way that God becomes real and holy to other people through your actions.

We learn in the Torah that we are supposed to be holy because God is holy (*Lev.* 19.2) and that the Jewish People is supposed to be a holy nation (*Ex.* 19.6). The Zohar makes it even clearer when it teaches, "We fill the earth with holiness through doing מִצְוֹת." How can doing מִצְוֹת fill the world with holiness?

קְדוּשָׁה

The Silent קְדוּשָׁה

1. אַתָּה קָדוֹשׁ וְשִׁמְךָ קָדוֹשׁ	You are HOLY and Your NAME is HOLY
2. וּקְדוֹשִׁים בְּכָל־יוֹם יְהַלְלוּךָ סֶּלָה.	and HOLINESS comes in praising You every day. Selah.
3. בָּרוּךְ אַתָּה יי הָאֵל הַקָּדוֹשׁ.	Blessed are You, ADONAI, The God, The HOLY (One).

Shabbat Morning קְדוּשָׁה

4. נְקַדֵּשׁ אֶת שִׁמְךָ בָּעוֹלָם	Let us make Your NAME HOLY in the Cosmos
5. כְּשֵׁם שֶׁמַּקְדִּישִׁים אוֹתוֹ	Just as they make it HOLY
6. בִּשְׁמֵי מָרוֹם	in the Heavens of the Heights—
7. כַּכָּתוּב עַל יַד נְבִיאֶךָ	As it is written by the hand of Your Prophet
8. וְקָרָא זֶה אֶל זֶה וְאָמַר:	"And they called, one to the other, and said:
9. קָדוֹשׁ קָדוֹשׁ קָדוֹשׁ יי צְבָאוֹת	HOLY, HOLY, HOLY is ADONAI of Hosts,
10. מְלֹא כָל־הָאָרֶץ כְּבוֹדוֹ.	all the world is full of God's HONOR."
11. אָז בְּקוֹל רַעַשׁ גָּדוֹל אַדִּיר וְחָזָק	Then in a voice, NOISY, BIG, KIND and STRONG
12. מַשְׁמִיעִים קוֹל	they make their voices heard
13. מִתְנַשְּׂאִים לְעֻמַּת שְׂרָפִים	lifted up toward the seraphim
14. לְעֻמָּתָם בָּרוּךְ יֹאמֵרוּ:	those facing the seraphim say, "BARUKH."
15. בָּרוּךְ כְּבוֹד יי מִמְּקוֹמוֹ.	Blessed be ADONAI's honor from God's Place.
16. מִמְּקוֹמְךָ מַלְכֵּנוּ	From Your Place, our Ruler
17. תוֹפִיעַ וְתִמְלוֹךְ עָלֵינוּ	Appear to us and Rule over us
18. כִּי מְחַכִּים אֲנַחְנוּ לָךְ.	because we wait for You.

מָתַי תִּמְלוֹךְ בְּצִיּוֹן	.19	When will You rule in Zion?
בְּקָרוֹב בְּיָמֵינוּ	.20	Soon? In our days?
לְעוֹלָם וָעֶד תִּשְׁכּוֹן.	.21	Forever and ever come. Be our neighbor.
תִּתְגַּדַּל וְתִתְקַדַּשׁ	.22	Be made Great and be made HOLY
בְּתוֹךְ יְרוּשָׁלַיִם עִירְךָ	.23	inside Jerusalem Your city
לְדוֹר וָדוֹר וּלְנֵצַח נְצָחִים.	.24	from generation to generation and from eternity to eternity.
וְעֵינֵינוּ תִרְאֶינָה	.25	And let our eyes see it—
מַלְכוּתֶךָ כַּדָּבָר הָאָמוּר	.26	Your Kingdom as it is said
בְּשִׁירֵי עֻזֶּךָ	.27	in the songs of Your strength
עַל יְדֵי דָוִד	.28	written by the hand of David
מְשִׁיחַ צִדְקֶךָ.	.29	the Annointed One of Your Righteousness.
יִמְלוֹךְ יי לְעוֹלָם אֱלֹהַיִךְ צִיּוֹן	.30	ADONAI, Rule forever, You are the God of Zion
לְדֹר וָדֹר הַלְלוּיָהּ.	.31	from generation to generation. Hallelujah.
לְדוֹר וָדוֹר נַגִּיד גָּדְלֶךָ	.32	From generation to generation we will tell of Your greatness
וּלְנֵצַח נְצָחִים קְדֻשָּׁתְךָ נַקְדִּישׁ.	.33	and from eternity to eternity Your holiness we make HOLY
וְשִׁבְחֲךָ אֱלֹהֵינוּ	.34	and Your Praise, Our God,
מִפִּינוּ לֹא יָמוּשׁ	.35	doesn't stop flowing from our mouths
לְעוֹלָם וָעֶד	.36	forever and ever.
כִּי אֵל מֶלֶךְ גָּדוֹל	.37	Because You are The God, The Ruler, The Great One
וְקָדוֹשׁ אָתָּה.	.38	and The Holy One.
בָּרוּךְ אַתָּה יי הָאֵל הַקָּדוֹשׁ.	.39	Blessed are You, ADONAI, The God, The HOLY One.

Can you see the three letters קדש in these words?

קָדְשָׁנוּ   מְקַדֵשׁ   קָדוֹשׁ

Holy = קָדוֹשׁ

makes Holy = מְקַדֵשׁ

made us Holy = קָדְשָׁנוּ

ROOT ANALYSIS

קדשׁ

Practice these phrases and circle all the words that contain the root קדשׁ.

אֲשֶׁר קִדְשָׁנוּ בְּמִצְוֹתָיו וְצִוָּנוּ	בָּרוּךְ אַתָּה יי הָאֵל הַקָּדוֹשׁ .1
וּבְדִבְרֵי קָדְשְׁךָ כָּתוּב לֵאמֹר	בָּרוּךְ אַתָּה יי מְקַדֵשׁ הַשַּׁבָּת .2
מְלֹא כָל-הָאָרֶץ כְּבוֹדוֹ	קָדוֹשׁ קָדוֹשׁ קָדוֹשׁ יי צְבָאוֹת .3
אַתָּה קָדוֹשׁ וְשִׁמְךָ קָדוֹשׁ	וּקְדוֹשִׁים בְּכָל-יוֹם יְהַלְלוּךָ .4
נְקַדֵּשׁ אֶת-שִׁמְךָ בָּעוֹלָם כְּשֵׁם שֶׁמַּקְדִישִׁים אוֹתוֹ בִּשְׁמֵי מָרוֹם .5	
תִּתְגַּדַּל וְתִתְקַדַּשׁ בְּתוֹךְ יְרוּשָׁלַיִם עִירְךָ לְדוֹר וָדוֹר .6	
נַעֲרִיצְךָ וְנַקְדִּישְׁךָ כְּסוֹד שִׂיחַ שַׂרְפֵי קֹדֶשׁ הַמַּקְדִישִׁים שִׁמְךָ .7	

Write in the missing letters for these words that are built from the root קדשׁ.

מְקַדֵּ___ .10   ___ְ___ָׁדוּשָׁה .9   קָ___ושׁ .8

66

Review the vocabulary and make your best guess at the meaning of the silent קְדוּשָׁה.

יוֹם

הלל

קָדֹשׁ

Take your best guess at the meaning of this text. Your teacher will help you with your translation.

אַתָּה קָדוֹשׁ וְשִׁמְךָ קָדוֹשׁ
וּקְדוֹשִׁים בְּכָל־יוֹם יְהַלְלוּךָ סֶלָה.
בָּרוּךְ אַתָּה יי הָאֵל הַקָּדוֹשׁ.

_____

_____

_____

_____

word parts		words	
in = בְּ	and = וְ	God = אֵל	name = שֵׁם
the = הַ	your = ךָ		all = כָּל

Use this Jacob's Ladder to practice these phrases from the קְדוּשָׁה.

1. תִּתְגַּדֵּל וְתִתְקַדַּשׁ בְּתוֹךְ יְרוּשָׁלַיִם עִירְךָ

2. כְּשֵׁם שֶׁמַּקְדִישִׁים אוֹתוֹ בִּשְׁמֵי מָרוֹם

3. כַּכָּתוּב עַל יַד נְבִיאֶךָ וְקָרָא זֶה אֶל זֶה וְאָמַר

4. אַתָּה קָדוֹשׁ וְשִׁמְךָ קָדוֹשׁ וּקְדוֹשִׁים

5. קָדוֹשׁ קָדוֹשׁ קָדוֹשׁ יי צְבָאוֹת

6. בָּרוּךְ כְּבוֹד יי מִמְּקוֹמוֹ

7. יִמְלֹךְ יי לְעוֹלָם אֱלֹהַיִךְ צִיּוֹן

8. לְדוֹר וָדוֹר נַגִּיד גָּדְלֶךָ וּלְנֵצַח נְצָחִים

9. מַלְכוּתְךָ כַּדָּבָר הָאָמוּר

10. מִמְּקוֹמְךָ מַלְכֵּנוּ תוֹפִיעַ וְתִמְלוֹךְ עָלֵינוּ

11. בָּרוּךְ אַתָּה יי הָאֵל הַקָּדוֹשׁ

12. אָז בְּקוֹל רַעַשׁ גָּדוֹל אַדִּיר וְחָזָק מַשְׁמִיעִים קוֹל

Can you see the three letters כבד in these words?

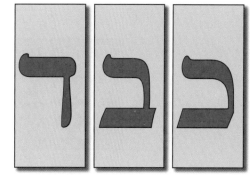

ROOT ANALYSIS

כָּבוֹד   כָּבֵד   כָּבֵד

honor = כָּבוֹד

heavy = כָּבֵד

liver = כָּבֵד

Practice these phrases and circle all the words that contain the root כבד.

1. כַּבֵּד אֶת־אָבִיךָ וְאֶת־אִמֶּךָ   בָּרוּךְ שֵׁם כְּבוֹד מַלְכוּתוֹ לְעוֹלָם וָעֶד

2. קָדוֹשׁ קָדוֹשׁ קָדוֹשׁ יי צְבָאוֹת מְלֹא כָל־הָאָרֶץ כְּבוֹדוֹ

TRANSLATION

Review the vocabulary and make your best guess at the meaning of this part of the קְדוּשָׁה.

word parts	words
His = וֹ∎	Adonai = יי
	Hosts = צְבָאוֹת
	full = מְלֹא
	all = כֹּל

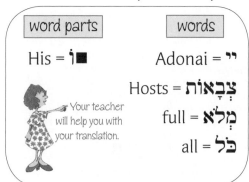
Your teacher will help you with your translation.

כבד

אֶרֶץ

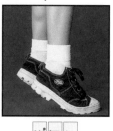

קָדֹשׁ

קָדוֹשׁ קָדוֹשׁ קָדוֹשׁ יי צְבָאוֹת מְלֹא כָל־הָאָרֶץ כְּבוֹדוֹ.

_____

_____

Review the vocabulary and make your best guess at the meaning of this part of the קְדוּשָׁה.

הלל   עוֹלָם   מֶלֶךְ

Take your best guess at the meaning of this text. Your teacher will help you with your translation.

יִמְלֹךְ יי לְעוֹלָם אֱלֹהַיִךְ צִיּוֹן לְדֹר וָדֹר הַלְלוּיָהּ.

_____

_____

_____

word parts	words
to = לְ	Zion = צִיּוֹן Adonai = יי
your = ךְ	generation = דֹר God = אֱלֹהִים
and = וָ	

Wrestling with Holiness

Jacob wrestled with a stranger all night. The two struggled with each other when morning started to break. The stranger said, "Let me go, for the day is breaking." Jacob said to him, "Are you a thief or a kidnapper that you are afraid of the morning?" He answered: "I am an angel." My one chance to praise the Eternal had not come until today."

"Angels are divided into two groups. Three groups of angels sing praises to the Eternal daily. The first group sings "קָדוֹשׁ." The second group also sings, "קָדוֹשׁ." And the third group sings, "קָדוֹשׁ, יי צְבָאוֹת." Every day new angels praise God.

Hullin 91b

Questions

1. Why did the angel need to stop wrestling in the morning?
2. What does this story teach us the importance of the קְדוּשָׁה?
3. How can we be like that angel when we say the קְדוּשָׁה?

קְדוּשַׁת הַיּוֹם

The Middle בְּרָכוֹת

The עֲמִידָה is like a sandwich. On the outside are sets of three בְּרָכוֹת, three praise בְּרָכוֹת at the beginning and three thanksgiving בְּרָכוֹת at the end. During the week there are thirteen petition בְּרָכוֹת in the middle. Petition means "asking." During the week we ask God for the things that we need. On Shabbat we don't do "business" with God. We remove these middle בְּרָכוֹת and replace them with a Shabbat prayer.

Shabbat

On Shabbat we say a בְּרָכָה called קְדוּשַׁת הַיּוֹם, "the Holiness of the Day." This is very much like the קִדּוּשׁ. It celebrates Shabbat as an opportunity to experience God's holiness and create a sense of holiness of our own.

וְשָׁמְרוּ

The Shabbat commandment was read in the middle of this prayer. But in a period of time when *some* people began to believe that the Ten Commandments were the only important part of the Torah, the Rabbis made a switch. In the evening service they used the וַיְכֻלּוּ, a piece of Torah that comes from the Shabbat part of the story of Creation (*Gen.* 2.1-3). On Saturday morning they used the וְשָׁמְרוּ (*Ex.* 31.16-17), which is a lesson about Shabbat that Moses taught soon after the Golden Calf incident.

72

קְדוּשַׁת הַיּוֹם

1.	וְשָׁמְרוּ בְנֵי יִשְׂרָאֵל אֶת־הַשַּׁבָּת
The Families-of-Israel shall KEEP SHABBAT	
2.	לַעֲשׂוֹת אֶת־הַשַּׁבָּת
to MAKE SHABBAT	
3.	לְדֹרֹתָם בְּרִית עוֹלָם.
in every generation as a forever COVENANT.	
4.	בֵּינִי וּבֵין בְּנֵי יִשְׂרָאֵל
Between Me and the Families-of-Israel	
5.	אוֹת הִיא לְעֹלָם.
SHABBAT is a forever sign.	
6.	כִּי שֵׁשֶׁת יָמִים עָשָׂה יי
Because in six days ADONAI MADE	
7.	אֶת־הַשָּׁמַיִם וְאֶת־הָאָרֶץ.
heavens and earth,	
8.	וּבַיּוֹם הַשְּׁבִיעִי
but on The Seventh Day	
9.	שָׁבַת וַיִּנָּפַשׁ.
God had a SHABBAT and re-SOULED.	
10.	אֱלֹהֵינוּ וֵאלֹהֵי אֲבוֹתֵינוּ
Our God and God of our Ancestors	
11.	רְצֵה בִמְנוּחָתֵנוּ.
enjoy our REST.	
12.	קַדְּשֵׁנוּ בְּמִצְוֹתֶיךָ
Make us Holy through Your MITZVOT	
13.	וְתֵן חֶלְקֵנוּ בְּתוֹרָתֶךָ
and give us a piece of Your TORAH.	
14.	שַׂבְּעֵנוּ מִטּוּבֶךָ
NOURISH us with Your goodness	
15.	וְשַׂמְּחֵנוּ בִּישׁוּעָתֶךָ
And MAKE-US-HAPPY through Your REDEMPTION	
16.	וְטַהֵר לִבֵּנוּ לְעָבְדְּךָ בֶּאֱמֶת.
PURIFY our hearts to Your WORK in truth.	
17.	וְהַנְחִילֵנוּ יי אֱלֹהֵינוּ
ADONAI our God, give-us-as-an-INHERITANCE	
18.	בְּאַהֲבָה וּבְרָצוֹן
in LOVE and because You WANT it—	
19.	שַׁבַּת קָדְשֶׁךָ
Your HOLY SHABBAT.	
20.	וְיָנוּחוּ בָהּ יִשְׂרָאֵל מְקַדְּשֵׁי שְׁמֶךָ.
May Israel REST on it MAKING Your NAME holy.	
21.	בָּרוּךְ אַתָּה יי מְקַדֵּשׁ הַשַּׁבָּת.
Blessed be You, ADONAI, the One-Who-makes SHABBAT HOLY.	

Review the vocabulary and make your best guess at the meaning of the first part of the וְשָׁמְרוּ.

עֹשֶׂה

שַׁבָּת

יִשְׂרָאֵל

בָּנִים

שׁוֹמֵר

עוֹלָם

Take your best guess at the meaning of this text. Your teacher will help you with your translation.

וְשָׁמְרוּ בְנֵי יִשְׂרָאֵל אֶת־הַשַׁבָּת
לַעֲשׂוֹת אֶת־הַשַׁבָּת לְדֹרֹתָם בְּרִית עוֹלָם.
בֵּינִי וּבֵין בְּנֵי יִשְׂרָאֵל אוֹת הִיא לְעֹלָם.

אוֹתִיוֹת

_____

_____

_____

word parts	words
to = לְ	generation = דֹרֹת
the = הַ	covenant = בְּרִית
and = וְ\וּ	between = בֵּין
me = יִ◼	she (Shabbat) = הִיא

Can you see the three letters שבת in these words?

שַׁבָּת יִשְׁבַּת שָׁבַת

Shabbat = שַׁבָּת

cease work = יִשְׁבַּת

(He) rested = שָׁבַת

ROOT ANALYSIS

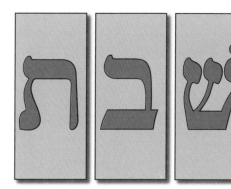

Practice these phrases and circle all the words that contain the root שבת.

1. וְשָׁמְרוּ בְנֵי־יִשְׂרָאֵל אֶת־הַשַּׁבָּת   כִּי בוֹ שָׁבַת צוּר עוֹלָמִים

2. וַיִּשְׁבֹּת בַּיּוֹם הַשְּׁבִיעִי מִכָּל־מְלַאכְתּוֹ אֲשֶׁר עָשָׂה

Can you see the three letters נפש in these words?

נֶפֶשׁ נַפְשְׁךָ וַיִּנָּפַשׁ

soul = נֶפֶשׁ

your soul = נַפְשְׁךָ

and He rested = וַיִּנָּפַשׁ

Practice these phrases and circle all the words that contain the root נפש.

3. יְדִיד נֶפֶשׁ אָב הָרַחֲמָן   וּבַיּוֹם הַשְּׁבִיעִי שָׁבַת וַיִּנָּפַשׁ

4. וְאָהַבְתָּ אֵת יי אֱלֹהֶיךָ בְּכָל־לְבָבְךָ וּבְכָל־נַפְשְׁךָ וּבְכָל־מְאֹדֶךָ

Review the vocabulary and make your best guess at the meaning of the second part of the וְשָׁמְרוּ.

שֶׁבַע   אֶרֶץ   עָשָׂה   יוֹם   שֵׁשׁ

שׁבת

Take your best guess at the meaning of this text. Your teacher will help you with your translation.

כִּי שֵׁשֶׁת יָמִים עָשָׂה יי
אֶת־הַשָּׁמַיִם וְאֶת־הָאָרֶץ
וּבַיּוֹם הַשְּׁבִיעִי שָׁבַת וַיִּנָּפַשׁ.

נ פ שׁ

_____

_____

_____

_____

word parts	words
the = הַ	because = כִּי
and = וְ\וּ	heavens = שָׁמַיִם
in/with = בְּ	

76

Shabbat in Egypt

Moses came and told Pharaoh to "Let my people go." Pharaoh laughed and said "No." To make matters worse, Pharaoh then told the Families-of-Israel that they had to work harder. Before they had to make mud bricks using straw that other people had cut and brought to the river's edge. Now the Jews had to make the same number of bricks every day, but they had to cut and haul their own straw. The Families-of-Israel got really mad at Moses because he had not set them free. Instead, he made things worse.

Moses went back to Pharaoh and asked, "How would you like to get twice as much work out of your slaves?" Pharaoh nodded. Moses said, "You have a choice. Kill more and more of your slaves by working them to death or give them one day a week off to recover. Then you can work them twice as hard." Pharaoh asked, "What day should it be?" Moses smiled and said, "Start on Friday night." From that day on, Israel had Shabbat in Egypt. It was their first taste of freedom (*Exodus Rabbah* 1.28).

Questions

1. What is the connection between Shabbat and Egypt?
2. How can knowing this story help you point your heart when you say both the קִדּוּשׁ and the קְדוּשַּׁת הַיּוֹם (with וְשָׁמְרוּ) on Shabbat?

בִּרְכַּת הוֹדָאָה

The Final Three

The עֲמִידָה ends with three final בְּרָכוֹת that are blessings of "thanksgiving." These final three are said on both Shabbat and weekdays. They are:

- בְּרְכַּת עֲבוֹדָה, which thanks God for hearing our prayers and hopes that our worship is acceptable.

- בִּרְכַּת הוֹדָאָה (or מוֹדִים), which thanks God for the opportunity to say thank you.

- בְּרְכַּת שָׁלוֹם, which thanks God for the possibility of peace (and asks God to help us finally achieve peace).

מוֹדִים

בִּרְכַּת הוֹדָאָה starts with the words "מוֹדִים אֲנַחְנוּ לָךְ." It means "We are thankful to You." These words lead us to the heart of this prayer: that God is the source of our lives and of all that is good in our lives.

בִּרְכַּת הוֹדָאָה was part of the original service in the Temple. At the end of a day of sacrificing the priests would say a few prayers that included the Ten Commandments, the שְׁמַע, the "מוֹדִים," and the priestly blessing for peace. When the Rabbis replaced sacrifices with the prayer service, מוֹדִים was still used as part of the ending.

בִּרְכַּת הוֹדָאָה thanks God for four things: our lives; our souls; the miracles in our lives; and the gifts that happen evening, morning and afternoon.

בִּרְכַּת הוֹדָאָה

1. מוֹדִים אֲנַחְנוּ לָךְ	We give THANKS to YOU
2. שָׁאַתָּה הוּא יי אֱלֹהֵינוּ	that YOU are the ONE, ADONAI our God
3. וֵאלֹהֵי אֲבוֹתֵינוּ לְעוֹלָם וָעֶד	and the God of our ancestors forever and always.
4. צוּר חַיֵּינוּ מָגֵן יִשְׁעֵנוּ	YOU are the rock of our lives, the shield of our future.
5. אַתָּה הוּא לְדוֹר וָדוֹר.	YOU are the ONE from generation to generation.
6. נוֹדֶה לְךָ וּנְסַפֵּר תְּהִלָּתֶךָ	We give THANKS to YOU and tell stories that celebrate YOU,
7. עַל חַיֵּינוּ הַמְּסוּרִים בְּיָדֶךָ	(a) For our LIVES that are delivered into YOUR hands
8. וְעַל נִשְׁמוֹתֵינוּ הַפְּקוּדוֹת לָךְ	(b) For our SOULS that visit YOU
9. וְעַל נִסֶּיךָ שֶׁבְּכָל־יוֹם עִמָּנוּ	(c) For YOUR MIRACLES that are with us every day
10. וְעַל נִפְלְאוֹתֶיךָ וְטוֹבוֹתֶיךָ	and (d) for YOUR WONDERS and YOUR GOOD STUFF
11. שֶׁבְּכָל־עֵת עֶרֶב וָבֹקֶר וְצָהֳרָיִם.	that are happening all the time, evening, morning and noon.
12. הַטּוֹב כִּי לֹא כָלוּ רַחֲמֶיךָ	The GOOD THING is that YOUR MERCY has never ended,
13. וְהַמְרַחֵם כִּי לֹא תַמּוּ חֲסָדֶיךָ	and in mercy that YOU don't remove YOUR KINDNESS
14. מֵעוֹלָם קִוִּינוּ לָךְ.	to eternity we are lined up with YOU.
15. וְעַל כֻּלָּם	For all this
16. יִתְבָּרַךְ וְיִתְרוֹמַם שִׁמְךָ מַלְכֵּנוּ	May YOUR NAME be blessed and made great, our Ruler
17. תָּמִיד לְעוֹלָם וָעֶד.	constantly forever and always.
18. וְכֹל הַחַיִּים יוֹדוּךָ סֶּלָה	And all life praises YOU. Selah.
19. וִיהַלְלוּ אֶת־שִׁמְךָ בֶּאֱמֶת	And may YOUR NAME be celebrated with truth.
20. הָאֵל יְשׁוּעָתֵנוּ וְעֶזְרָתֵנוּ סֶלָה.	You are THE GOD, our SAVIOR, and our HELPER. Selah.
21. בָּרוּךְ אַתָּה יי הַטּוֹב שִׁמְךָ	Blessed are YOU, ADONAI, the ONE whose NAME is GOOD
22. וּלְךָ נָאֶה לְהוֹדוֹת.	and to YOU it is right to SAY THANKS.

Review the vocabulary and make your best guess at the meaning of the first line of בִּרְכַּת הוֹדָאָה.

אָב

הוּא

אַתָּה

אֲנַחְנוּ

מוֹדֶה

עוֹלָם

מוֹדִים אֲנַחְנוּ לָךְ שָׁאַתָּה הוּא יי אֱלֹהֵינוּ
וֵאלֹהֵי אֲבוֹתֵינוּ לְעוֹלָם וָעֶד.

_____

_____

_____

Your teacher will help you with your translation.

word parts	words
that/which = שֶׁ/שָׁ	and more = וָעֶד
	to you = לָךְ

The Choreography

The Talmud teaches that we are required to bow at the beginning and the end of בִּרְכַּת הוֹדָאָה as a way of acknowledging God's presence in our lives. We are told that if someone does not bend when he or she says מוֹדִים, his or her spine will turn into a snake.

Rashi explains that this does not mean that a person's spine will grow soft and bend. Rather, it means that he or she will become like the snake in the Adam and Eve story. The snake tried to convince Eve that what God wanted did not make a difference. He told her to do what she wanted to do rather than be grateful for everything that God did. When we don't bow before God and say "thank you," we become the snake (*Brakhot* 34a).

Question: What does it mean to become the snake?

80

David's Memory Makes a Difference

David took the city of Jerusalem and wanted to build God's House there, but God said "No." God was upset about all the blood that David had spilled. God was also upset that he had done a bad thing in stealing Batsheva from her husband. David asked, "Will you ever forgive me?" God answered, "Eventually, but your son, Solomon, will be the one to build the Temple."

When the Temple was finished and ready for its dedication, Solomon tried to bring the Ark of the Covenant into the Holy of Holies. The gates refused to open. Solomon said, "Lift up your heads. Open up the gates. Let in the Ruler with Honor *(Psalms 24:9-10)*". The gates stayed shut and asked him, "Who is the Ruler with Honor?" Solomon said, "The Ten Commandments that are in the Ark." The gates said, "Try again." Solomon said, "The Holy One Who often comes close to us when we are near the Ark." The gates didn't move and said, "What is your third guess?" Solomon said, "David, my father, who was God's servant." The gates opened. The Ark went into the Holy of Holies. David was forgiven, and the angels sang, "בָּרוּךְ אַתָּה יי הַטּוֹב שִׁמְךָ וּלְךָ נָאֶה לְהוֹדוֹת, Praised are You, Adonai, The Good-One is Your name and it feels good to praise You." *(Shabbat 30a; Shibbolei ha-Leket 18)*

Questions

1. The end of this story shows that God forgave David. Why did the angels sing "It feels good to praise God"? (Clue: Remember, David wrote the Psalms—Songs of Praise.)
2. How does knowing this story help you point your heart when you say בִּרְכַּת הוֹדָאָה?

בִּרְכַּת שָׁלוֹם

בִּרְכַּת שָׁלוֹם is:
- the last of three thanksgiving בְּרָכוֹת that end the עֲמִידָה and the very last בְּרָכָה in the עֲמִידָה.
- a בְּרָכָה that asks for both world peace and personal inner peace.

- a prayer that has two versions. In Ashkenazic traditions, שִׂים שָׁלוֹם is said at morning services. שָׁלוֹם רָב is said at afternoon, מוּסָף and evening services. Sefardim do it differently.

At the end of the service in the Temple the כֹּהֲנִים (priests) would bless the people. This was their way of performing a biblical מִצְוָה, "The כֹּהֲנִים should put My Name on the People of Israel—and I will bless them" (Num. 6.27). שָׁלוֹם is one of God's names.

This was done as part of a ceremony called *duchinin*. The כֹּהֲנִים would come up on the bimah, cover their heads with their tallitot, spread their fingers making a "שׁ"— and say the words of the priestly benediction. This ceremony is still done weekly in some Orthodox synagogues in Israel and Sefardic synagogues. In some Conservative and Orthodox synagogues elsewhere this is done only on festivals. Many Reform synagogues have dropped the ceremony, but Reform rabbis often still bless the congregation with these words at the end of services. Jewish parents still use this biblical בְּרָכָה to bless their children on Shabbat.

When the Temple was destroyed and the עֲמִידָה replaced the sacrifices, בִּרְכַּת שָׁלוֹם became its final בְּרָכָה. בִּרְכַּת שָׁלוֹם became the day-to-day replacement for בִּרְכַּת-כֹּהֲנִים in the Temple. This pattern followed a lesson taught by Rabbi Eleazar ha-Kappar, "Great is peace. It is the end of all בְּרָכוֹת" (*Sifrei, Numbers*, 42).

שִׂים שָׁלוֹם

1.	שִׂים שָׁלוֹם (בָּעוֹלָם) טוֹבָה וּבְרָכָה
	Put PEACE, GOODNESS & BLESSING
2.	חֵן וָחֶסֶד וְרַחֲמִים
	FAVOR, KINDNESS and MERCY
3.	עָלֵינוּ וְעַל כָּל־יִשְׂרָאֵל עַמֶּךָ.
	on us and on all Israel, Your people.
4.	בָּרְכֵנוּ אָבִינוּ כֻּלָּנוּ כְּאֶחָד
	BLESS us, our PARENT, all of us as ONE
5.	בְּאוֹר פָּנֶיךָ,
	in the light of YOUR FACE
6.	כִּי בְאוֹר פָּנֶיךָ נָתַתָּ לָּנוּ
	because in the light of YOUR FACE You gave us,
7.	יְיָ אֱלֹהֵינוּ
	ADONAI, our God,
8.	תּוֹרַת חַיִּים וְאַהֲבַת חֶסֶד,
	The TORAH of life, and the LOVE-of-KINDNESS
9.	וּצְדָקָה וּבְרָכָה וְרַחֲמִים
	and JUSTICE and BLESSING and MERCY
10.	וְחַיִּים וְשָׁלוֹם.
	and LIFE and PEACE.
11.	וְטוֹב בְּעֵינֶיךָ
	And (may it be) good in YOUR EYES
12.	לְבָרֵךְ אֶת עַמְּךָ יִשְׂרָאֵל
	to bless Your people Israel
13.	בְּכָל־עֵת וּבְכָל־שָׁעָה בִּשְׁלוֹמֶךָ.
	in all times, in all hours, with Your PEACE.
14.	בָּרוּךְ אַתָּה יְיָ
	Praised be You, ADONAI,
15.	הַמְבָרֵךְ אֶת־עַמּוֹ יִשְׂרָאֵל בַּשָּׁלוֹם.
	The ONE-Who-BLESSES God's people Israel with PEACE.

Can you see the three letters שלם in these words?

ROOT ANALYSIS

מְשַׁלֵם שְׁלֵמָה שָׁלוֹם

peace = שָׁלוֹם

complete = שְׁלֵמָה

pay = מְשַׁלֵם

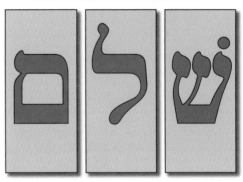

Practice these phrases and circle all the words that contain the root שלם.

1. עוֹשֶׂה שָׁלוֹם בִּמְרוֹמָיו

2. שָׁלוֹם רָב עַל־יִשְׂרָאֵל עַמְּךָ

3. בָּרוּךְ מְשַׁלֵם שָׂכָר טוֹב לִירֵאָיו

4. אָבִינוּ מַלְכֵּנוּ, שְׁלַח רְפוּאָה שְׁלֵמָה לְפָנֶיךָ

5. בְּסֵפֶר חַיִּים בְּרָכָה וְשָׁלוֹם וּפַרְנָסָה טוֹבָה

6. בּוֹאֲכֶם לְשָׁלוֹם מַלְאֲכֵי הַשָּׁלוֹם מַלְאֲכֵי עֶלְיוֹן

7. וּשְׁמֹר צֵאתֵנוּ וּבוֹאֵנוּ לְחַיִּים וּלְשָׁלוֹם מֵעַתָּה וְעַד עוֹלָם.

8. שִׂים שָׁלוֹם טוֹבָה וּבְרָכָה חֵן וָחֶסֶד וְרַחֲמִים

84

Review the vocabulary and make your best guess at the meaning of the first half of שִׂים שָׁלוֹם.

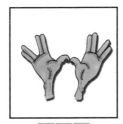

עַל חֶסֶד בָּרֵךְ טוֹב שָׁלוֹם

Take your best guess at the meaning of this text. Your teacher will help you with your translation.

שִׂים שָׁלוֹם טוֹבָה וּבְרָכָה חֵן וָחֶסֶד
וְרַחֲמִים עָלֵינוּ וְעַל כָּל־יִשְׂרָאֵל עַמֶּךָ

_____

_____

_____

word parts		words	
us = נוּ	and = וְ/וָ	mercy = רַחֲמִים	put = שִׂים
	your = ךָ	nation = עַם	favor = חֵן

85

Review the vocabulary and make your best guess at the meaning of the second half of שִׂים שָׁלוֹם.

שָׁלֵם

יִשְׂרָאֵל

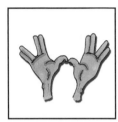

ברך

עֵינַיִם

טוֹב

Take your best guess at the meaning of this text. Your teacher will help you with your translation.

וְטוֹב בְּעֵינֶיךָ לְבָרֵךְ אֶת־עַמְּךָ יִשְׂרָאֵל

בְּכָל־עֵת וּבְכָל־שָׁעָה בִּשְׁלוֹמֶךָ.

בָּרוּךְ אַתָּה יי הַמְבָרֵךְ אֶת־עַמּוֹ יִשְׂרָאֵל בַּשָּׁלוֹם.

_____

_____

_____

_____

word parts		words	
your = ךָ	to/for = לְ	nation = עַם	season = עֵת
in/with = בְּ	and = וְ/וּ	all = כָּל	time = שָׁעָה

86

Can you see the three letters עשה in these words?

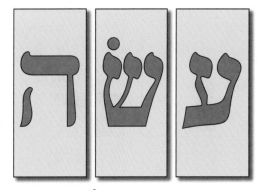

עוֹשֶׂה   יַעֲשֶׂה   מַעֲשֶׂיךָ

make = עוֹשֶׂה

will make = יַעֲשֶׂה

your makings = מַעֲשֶׂיךָ

Practice these phrases and circle all the words that contain the root עשה.

הוּא יַעֲשֶׂה שָׁלוֹם עָלֵינוּ	עֹשֶׂה שָׁלוֹם בִּמְרוֹמָיו .1
כֻּלָּם בְּחָכְמָה עָשִׂיתָ	מָה רַבּוּ מַעֲשֶׂיךָ יי .2

Can you see the three letters אמן in these words?

אָמֵן   אֱמוּנָה   נֶאֱמָן

 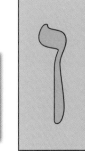  

So be it! = אָמֵן

faith = אֱמוּנָה

faithful = נֶאֱמָן

Practice these phrases and circle all the words that contain the root אמן.

הָאֵל הַנֶּאֱמָן הָאוֹמֵר וְעוֹשֶׂה	וּבִזְמַן קָרִיב וְנֹאמַר אָמֵן .3
וּמְקַיֵּם אֱמוּנָתוֹ לִישֵׁנֵי עָפָר	יי אֱלֹהִים וְנֶאֱמָנִים דְּבָרֶיךָ .4

87

Review the vocabulary and make your best guess at the meaning of עֹשֶׂה שָׁלוֹם.

אָמֵן

יִשְׂרָאֵל

עַל

שָׁלוֹם

עֹשֶׂה

Take your best guess at the meaning of this text. Your teacher will help you with your translation.

words

בִּמְרוֹמָיו = in His heavens

הוּא = He

כָּל = all

וְאִמְרוּ = and let us say

word parts

בְּ = in/with

וְ = and

עֹשֶׂה שָׁלוֹם בִּמְרוֹמָיו
הוּא יַעֲשֶׂה שָׁלוֹם עָלֵינוּ
וְעַל כָּל־יִשְׂרָאֵל וְאִמְרוּ אָמֵן.

_____

_____

_____

_____

Choreography

At the end of the עֲמִידָה, during the saying of עֹשֶׂה שָׁלוֹם, a person:

- takes three steps backwards
- bows to the left (עֹשֶׂה שָׁלוֹם בִּמְרוֹמָיו)
- bows to the right (הוּא יַעֲשֶׂה שָׁלוֹם עָלֵינוּ)
- bows forward (וְעַל כָּל־יִשְׂרָאֵל וְאִמְרוּ אָמֵן)
- pauses for a moment before moving away.

When we take three steps backward we are like:

- a servant leaving a master or a citizen backing away from a monarch (O.H. 123.1).
- Moses leaving Mt. Sinai and going back through the cloud, the fog, and the darkness (Deut 4.11).

Moses leaving the burning bush and stepping back from the holy space. (Shibbolei ha-Leket).

When we bow to the right, left and forward we are acting out a scene.

- The angel Mikha'el stands to the right of God. He represents God, the strict judge Who follows all the rules.
- The angel Gavri'el stands to the left of God. He speaks for God's commitment to mercy—forgiving people and meeting their needs.

(Bet Yosef 123; Rabbi Eli Munk).

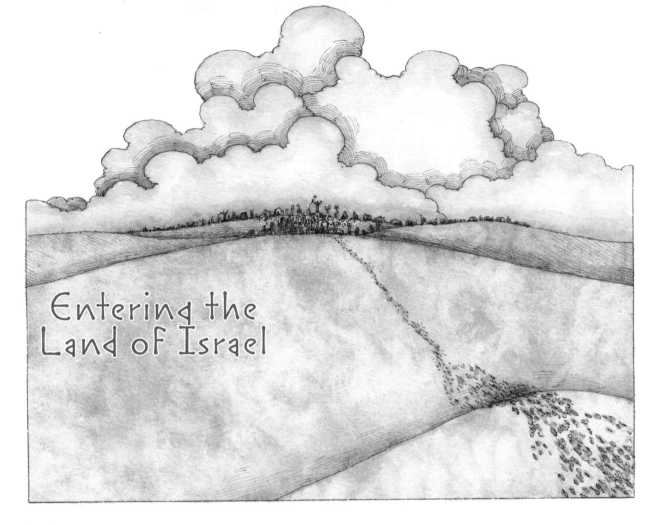

Entering the Land of Israel

It is not a long walk from Egypt to Israel, yet it took the Families-of-Israel forty years. It took a long time because it took the Families-of-Israel a long time to become a holy nation.

God could have led them along the Mediterranean. That is the quick way, but God chose a longer road. God said, "If I lead them directly into the Land of Israel, they will become selfish. These former slaves will only think about what they have and what they can have. They will worry about their own fields and their own vineyards, and they will forget to take care of each other. They will forget about the Torah. If they camp together in the wilderness--if they have to ration water and gather their own food every day—they will gain discipline and become a community."

Just about as soon as they crossed the Reed Sea the people complained about the lack of water. They were afraid that they would not have enough. God talked to them directly at Mount Sinai, and within two months they were making a Golden Calf. They were worried that no one was leading them. The rebellions kept coming. Even though there was more than enough miracle food, manna, the people complained about the lack of meat. Another time they complained about the lack of "garlic, onions, and fish that they used to eat for free in Egypt."

When God asked the families to spy out the Land of Israel, the people panicked. They chickened out. They stopped trusting God. No faith. They said, "We can't do it." God extended the training program. The Families-of-Israel spent forty years in Sinai. They gathered manna every day except Shabbat. They stood in line to get water. They studied Torah with Moses and used it to solve the problems that came with living together.

Finally, after all that waiting, God told them it was time to enter the Land. For forty years they had owned nothing. They had been homeless wanderers. They had rebelled and rebelled. When Joshua led Israel into the Land they spent seven years fighting. At the end of seven years they were sick of war. They had had enough. At that moment the angels looked into Israel's hearts. The angels saw that Israel had grown. They had learned to live together and trust God. They had come to understand that שָׁלוֹם was the most important thing. At that moment the angels sang for the first time, "בָּרוּךְ אַתָּה יי עֹשֶׂה הַשָּׁלוֹם" (*Shibbolei ha-Leket*, chapter 18 and other midrashim).

Questions

1. How did the years in the desert help the Families-of-Israel build up a sense of שָׁלוֹם?
2. When have you been like the Families-of-Israel, taking a long time to be ready to enter a "Promised Land"?
3. How can knowing this story help you point your heart when you say בִּרְכַּת שָׁלוֹם?